Published by Bassline Publishing
www.basslinepublishing.com

All music transcribed and engraved by Stuart Clayton
Additional harmonic transcription work by Tom O'Grady
Cover image supplied by Photoshot

ISBN 13: 978-0-9933727-0-4

# Notation Legend

**The Stave:** most music written for the bass guitar uses the bass clef. The example to the right shows the placement of the notes on the stave.

**Tablature:** this is a graphical representation of the music. Each horizontal line corresponds with a string on the bass guitar, with the lowest line representing the lowest string. The numbers represent the frets to be played. Numbers stacked vertically indicate notes that are played together. Where basses with five or six strings are required, the tablature stave will have five or six lines as necessary.

Notes shown in brackets indicated that a note has been tied over from a previous bar.

**Repeats:** the double line and double dot bar lines indicate that the music between these bar lines should be repeated. If the music is to be repeated more than once, a written indication will be given i.e. 'play 3x'.

**1st & 2nd Time Endings:** these are used for sections that are repeated, but which have different endings. The first ending is used the first time, the second is used on the repeat. The first ending is ignored on the repeat, only the second is used.

**Slap:** the note is slapped with the thumb.

**Pop:** the note is popped with either the first or second finger.

**Thumb Up:** played with an upstroke of the thumb.

**Fretting Hand:** played by hammering on with the fretting hand.

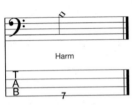

**Harmonic:** note is played as a harmonic by lighting touching the string above the fret indicated.

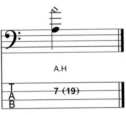

**Artificial Harmonic:** fret the lower note and tap the string over the fret shown in brackets.

**Trill:** alternate between the notes indicated by repeatedly hammering-on and pulling-off.

**Vibrato:** the pitch of the note is altered by repeatedly bending and releasing the string.

**Hammer-On:** only the first note is struck. The second is sounded by fretting it with another finger.

**Pull-Off:** Only the first note is struck. Lift the fretting finger to sound the second fretted note.

**Slide:** play the first note, then slide the finger to the second.

**Picking Hand Tap:** note is tapped with a finger of the picking hand. If necessary, the finger will be specified.

**Fretting Hand Tap:** note is tapped with a finger of the fretting hand. If necessary, the finger will be specified.

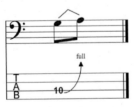

**Bend:** note is bent upwards to the interval indicated. ½ = semitone, full = tone.

**Bend and Release:** note is bent up to the interval indicated then released to the original note.

**Ghost Note:** note is a pitchless 'dead' note used as a rhythmic device.

**Accent:** note is accentuated, or played louder.

**Staccato:** note is played staccato - short.

**Tenuto:** note is held for its full length.

*p*   *piano* - played very softly
*mp*   *mezzo-piano* - played moderately quietly
*f*   *forte* - played loud/strong
*mf*   *mezzo forte* - played moderately loud/strong

**D.C al Coda:** Return to the beginning of the song and play until the bar marked Coda. Then jump to the section marked Coda.
**D.S al Coda:** Return to the sign, then play until the bar marked Coda. Then jump to the Coda.
**D.C (or D.S) al Fine:** Return to the point specified, then play until the Fine marking. Stop at this point

# CONTENTS

Introduction                          4

Biography                             6

Gear Breakdown                       12

Style Analysis                       16


**THE MUSIC**

Detroit                              34

Redemption                           48

Jekyll & Hyde                        64

Revelation                           78

Cee-Tee-Eye                          92

# Introduction

**Welcome to *Marcus Miller - Highlights from Renaissance*. This book contains highly detailed transcriptions of a selection of five songs, together with extensive performance notes, a biography, gear analysis and much more.**

The idea behind this book came in early 2015. I'd been a big fan of Marcus's *Renaissance* album since it was released and naturally, my thoughts soon turned to transcribing some of the tunes. Before long I had written out the lines from two favourites, 'Detroit' and 'Cee-Tee-Eye', both of which are great fun to play. Of course, I knew that a transcription book featuring these tunes would be popular, but I was also aware that the licensing for such a project would likely be difficult to organise, if not impossible. Thankfully, it turned out to be a lot quicker and easier than I had anticipated.

As with every book I write, I wanted to make this one as thorough as possible. That meant including a detailed biography, a gear analysis, a discography and an exhaustively researched analysis of Marcus's playing style. The result is the book you now hold in your hands, the product of almost a years worth of painstaking transcription and analysis work, research and more research. I loved every second of it.

This book would not have been possible without a few people, who deserve a great deal of thanks: Matt Smith and Charlotte Mortimer at Faber Music, Tom O'Grady for his invaluable help with the more challenging chords, Sire Guitars for the fantastic photography of Marcus's new line of instruments, Photoshot for the live photography, Fender for the images of the Marcus Miller Fender Signature model and Andy Casey for the excellent playing photography. I'd also like to thank my wife Laura for her continuing love and support, not to mention the fantastic front cover design.

I hope you enjoy this book.

**Stuart Clayton**
**November 2015**

# MARCUS MILLER
## BIOGRAPHY

Diversity is one of the keys to success as a professional musician and is a concept that Marcus Miller has certainly embraced throughout his career. Segueing effortlessly from the thriving late seventies New York studio scene into high-profile work with artists such as Miles Davis, Luther Vandross and David Sanborn, somehow Miller also found the time along the way to forge a solo career that has made him one of the world's most respected bassists. After more than thirty five years in the business, the multi-Grammy-winning bassist continues to push himself into new musical situations, through collaborations with operatic tenor Kenn Hicks, fellow bassists Stanley Clarke and Victor Wooten and with his most recent solo releases, *Renaissance* and *Afrodeezia*. Unsurprisingly, his popularity amongst bass players remains undiminished, resulting in him having - alongside the legendary Jaco Pastorius - one of the most recognisable and widely imitated voices on the instrument.

Marcus Miller was born in Brooklyn, New York on 14th June 1959 and brought up in the Jamaica district of Queens. Not only was he born into a musical family - his father was an organist and jazz pianist Wynton Kelly (best known for his work with Miles Davis) was his second cousin - but he also found himself surrounded by musicians in the local neighbourhood. Captivated by R&B acts such as The Jackson 5, Stevie Wonder and Kool & The Gang, he began his musical endeavours first by playing the piano and singing, then at the age of 10 learning to play the clarinet. Quickly realising that the clarinet was unlikely to land him a place in any of the local R&B groups, he went in search of a new instrument under the guidance of his music teacher Mr. Guarino. After trying his hand at the saxophone and piano, he finally found his instrument when his best friend was given a bass guitar. Realising that the bass was the foundation of the music that he loved, Miller now knew where he must focus his efforts and before long had his own bass, a semi hollow-bodied Univox.

Alongside his bass guitar studies, Marcus continued to hone his clarinet skills and was eventually awarded a place at the prestigious New York High School of Music & Art. From there he progressed to Queens College on a clarinet scholarship, supplementing his studies with bass gigs in the evenings. Studying the instrument during one of its most fertile periods, he had no shortage of inspiration, with bassists such as James Jamerson, Robert Bell (Kool & The Gang), Wilton Felder, Jaco Pastorius, Stanley Clarke and Larry Graham all having a strong influence on his playing. His school friend Kenny Washington also encouraged him to study jazz, introducing him to the work of Paul Chambers, Eddie Gomez and Ron Carter. Miller's jazz studies allowed him to significantly advance his understanding of harmony and composition.

### Early Career

Marcus's earliest pro gigs were with keys player Lonnie Liston Smith and Harlem River Drive, a band which also featured his cousin Ronnie Miller and drummer Omar Hakim. In 1977, Ronnie began working with renowned flute player Bobbi Humphrey and was quick to mention Marcus's name when she needed a new bass player. Soon after joining the band, Marcus wrote a song for her called 'Love When I'm In Your Arms'. Humphrey liked it and asked to record it on her next album, convincing producer Ralph MacDonald to use Marcus on the session (the rest of the album was recorded by Anthony Jackson). Impressed both with Marcus's playing and his reading skills, MacDonald began both employing and recommending the young bassist for studio work around New York. Starting with TV commercials and radio jingles, Marcus soon found himself working around the clock at studios all over the city. During this period he also began working with fellow Jamaica resident Lenny White, who was well-known for his work with Chick Corea and Return to Forever. Marcus initially toured with White and subsequently played on his solo albums *Big City* (1977) and *Streamline* (1978).

In 1978, after a successful audition arranged by Buddy Williams (drummer in Bobbi Humphrey's band), Marcus began playing for the Saturday Night Live TV show. It was here that he met saxophonist David Sanborn, with whom he struck up a friendship and began writing and recording. Miller played on Sanborn's 1981 release *Voyeur* as well as writing and co-writing a number of tracks. The slap bass-driven 'Run for Cover' in particular quickly became popular with bassists and has since become one of Miller's best-known compositions. This early recording of the track finds Miller on fine form, featuring a solid slap groove and a tasteful solo. Long time Miller fans will recognise that his heavily chorused bass sound on this track is quite different to the famous tone that he later developed on his Sadowsky-modified '77 Fender Jazz Bass.

During this period he also began working with jazz vocalist Roberta Flack, becoming friends with backing vocalist Luther Vandross in the process. Miller and Vandross began writing and demoing material together, beginning a collaboration that would not only make a superstar out of Vandross, but also see them writing material for Aretha Franklin's early eighties comeback. The Queen of Soul's Grammy-nominated song 'Jump To It' (from the 1982 album of the same name) was written by the pair and produced by Vandross.

In 1981 Marcus received a phone call from legendary jazz trumpet player Miles Davis asking if he could be at his studio in two hours. Miller agreed and found himself being auditioned to play on Davis' 1981 album *The Man With The Horn*, his first release in six years following a period of semiretirement. The success of this album was later followed by the live album *We Want Miles* in 1982, *Star People* in 1983 and *Tutu* in 1986. *Tutu* was significant for both Davis and Miller: Davis received the 1987 Best Jazz Instrumental Performance, Soloist Grammy for the album, while Miller wrote the majority of the material, played many of the instruments himself and co-produced the album alongside Tommy LiPuma.

ABOVE: Miles Davis' 1981 album *The Man with the Horn*

BELOW: *Tutu,* the Grammy-winning Miles Davis album from 1986

## Solo Career

Having now garnered an enviable reputation for himself as a first-call session bassist - not to mention as a writer, multi-instrumentalist and producer - Miller began to take steps to establish his own solo career. His first two solo offerings, *Suddenly* (1983) and *Marcus Miller* (1984) were commercial R&B albums with a focus on his song-writing and vocal skills. Both albums were under-promoted and were largely unsuccessful, despite containing strong material, as well as an impressive cast of musicians including frequent collaborators MacDonald, Sanborn and Vandross. Although these records are not essential listening in the same vein of much of his later work, several gems can still be found on them: the slapped intro of 'Superspy' and the slap/synth grooves of 'Juice' in particular stand out, as does his fretless work on 'Nadine'. Following the lack of commercial breakthrough of these albums, Miller began working with fellow Jamaica resident Lenny White in The Jamaica Boys and continued to focus on his

**ABOVE:** *The Sun Don't Lie*, **Marcus's 1993 solo album**

**BELOW:** *Tales*, **from 1995**

studio career. He also branched out into film scoring in the late eighties - his first film score was for the popular comedy *House Party* (1990), after which he worked on the Eddie Murphy comedy *Boomerang* (1992).

In 1993, nine years after his previous solo effort, Marcus wrote and recorded a third album, *The Sun Don't Lie*. Featuring a sophisticated collection of jazz and funk-influenced instrumental pieces, the album met with critical acclaim both amongst the bass community and a wider jazz audience, reaching #9 on the Billboard Contemporary Jazz Chart. Dedicated to the memory of Miles Davis (who passed away shortly before its release), the album featured guest appearances from a host of highly regarded musicians including Wayne Shorter (Weather Report), Vernon Reid (Living Colour), Joe Sample (The Crusaders) and Tony Williams (Miles Davis Band). As for the songs themselves, there was plenty for bass players to get their teeth into: from the opening solo phrases of 'Panther', to the infectious slap grooves of 'Rampage' and his stellar fretless work on 'Moons' it was clear that Miller was not just a first rate studio musician, but also one of the most engaging voices on the instrument. However, it was his slapped cover version of the Weather Report classic 'Teen Town' that drew the most admirers. Miller had been playing the bass-led tune as a lead-in to the commercial breaks on *Saturday Night Live* for some time and it had generated a considerable buzz amongst bass players. Traditionally a piece that would be played fingerstyle, Miller's highly developed slap technique allowed him to navigate the intricate, meandering melody with ease and without sacrificing the groove. Unsurprisingly, this piece has since become a favourite amongst his fanbase.

Marcus followed the success of *The Sun Don't Lie* with *Tales* in 1995. Seeking to focus specifically on his solo career for an extended period of time, Marcus took three months off from other commitments to write and record the album. Inspired to include elements of rap and hip-hop in his music, Marcus decided to build the album around the history of black music, using samples of renowned musicians speaking about their experiences with blues and music in general. Some of these he recorded himself, although he was also able to source interview footage of Miles Davis and Joe Zawinul and historical footage of jazz titans such as Duke Ellington, Lester Young and Charlie Parker through DJs and jazz archivists. *Tales* also featured collaborations with fellow bassist Me'Shell NdegéOcello on 'Rush Over' and vocalist Lalah Hathaway on 'Infatuation'.

Marcus remained busy throughout the remainder of the nineties: he produced legendary saxophonist Wayne Shorter's 1996 album *High Life* and formed the Legends band with Eric Clapton, David Sanborn, Joe Sample and Steve Gadd. He also released a live album, *Live and More* in 1998.

His next album, $M^2$, arrived in 2001. Dedicated to the memory of Grover Washington Jr., the record again featured a stellar cast of musicians including Herbie Hancock, Wayne Shorter, Chaka Khan, Raphael Saadiq, Branford Marsalis, Maceo Parker and Fred Wesley. Again inspired by hip-hop and rap, many of the pieces utilised slower tempos, allowing Marcus greater rhythmic flexibility in his playing - this is particularly evident in the album opener 'Power' where Marcus not only uses quick-fire double thumbed passages, but also adds rhythmic 'ghosting' between notes and phrases in the same way that a jazz drummer might play ghost notes on the snare drum. Inspired by the way artists such as Miles Davis and John Coltrane would play cover versions of their favourite songs, Miller began to do the same with this album, hoping to introduce a new generation to classics such as 'Red Baron' (Billy Cobham), 'Goodbye Pork Pie Hat' (Charles Mingus) and 'Lonnie's Lament' (John Coltrane). $M^2$ was also reflective of his movie scoring career: a string section was used on several songs, while 'Boomerang' was a development of a short piece that he had

ABOVE: Marcus playing
with fellow virtuoso
bassists Stanley Clarke
and Victor Wooten
in SMV

written for the 1992 Eddie Murphy movie of the same name and which had
been popular with his fanbase. Of course, there was plenty for bass players
to marvel at throughout, from the infectious bass riff of 'Power', the palm-
muted funk of '3 Deuces' to his astonishing hard-plucked solo on 'Red
Baron'.

In 2005 Marcus collaborated with operatic tenor Kenn Hicks on an *Avanti*,
an album of famous arias set against a jazz/gospel background. The project
had its roots in the late eighties, when Hicks had been recommended as a
vocal coach. After hearing Hicks singing an aria, Marcus told him he wanted
to record it in a jazz setting, setting in motion a project that would come
to fruition over fifteen years later. In the same year Marcus released a new
studio album, *Silver Rain*, the title track of which featured Eric Clapton, who
had written the song with Marcus whilst they were playing in the Legends
band. *Silver Rain* is notable for bass-driven tracks such as 'Bruce Lee' and
'La Villette' and cover versions of Edgar Winter's 'Frankenstein', Stevie
Wonder's 'Boogie On Reggae Woman' and Beethoven's 'Moonlight Sonata'.

In the latter part of the decade, Marcus began seeking out new challenges,
resulting in the formation of SMV, a bass-heavy supergroup with fellow low-
enders Stanley Clarke and Victor Wooten. The seeds for this venture had
been sown at *Bass Player Live* back in 2006 when Miller and Wooten had
joined Clarke on stage after presenting him with the magazine's Lifetime
Achievement Award. An album - *Thunder* - was released in 2008, featuring
new compositions alongside cover versions from the back catalogs of the
three bassists. The group, backed by a full band, toured successfully in the

**ABOVE:** *Tutu Revisited*, celebrating the classic Miles Davis album

**BELOW:** *Afrodeezia*, Marcus's 2015 album, written to raise awareness of the history of slavery

In 2010 Marcus toured to celebrate the twenty-fifth anniversary of Miles Davis' acclaimed album, *Tutu*. Recalling Davis' preference not to look to the past, Marcus decided to approach the project in a way that was respectful to Davis' habit of seeking out young musicians who would benefit from his experience. Recruiting a brand new band, Miller reworked and updated the tunes appropriately, the results of which can be heard on the stunning live album *Tutu Revisited* (2011).

Revitalised by the *Tutu Revisited* tour, Marcus decided to write his next album around his new group. The result was *Renaissance* (2012), arguably one of his best and complete statements as a solo artist. Largely eschewing cover versions this time around - aside from stunning versions of Weldon Irvine's 'Mr. Clean' and War's 'Slippin' Into Darkness' - the album featured a wide variety of music, from the slick funk of 'Detroit', the jazz-tinged ballad 'Septembro (Brazilian Wedding Song)', to the CTI record label-inspired 'Cee-Tee-Eye'. Marcus is on top-form throughout the album, soloing effortlessly with his highly developed slap technique on 'Detroit' and 'Mr. Clean', playing upright bass on 'February' and boasting flawless fretless and bass clarinet work on 'Gorée (Go-ray)'. This particular song was written following a visit to the island of Gorée, a former slave camp off of the coast of Senegal. Miller performed this piece during the *Renaissance* tour and after a show in Paris was approached by the director of UNESCO (the goodwill arm of the United Nations), impressed with the story behind the song. This meeting led to Miller taking on the role of Artist for Peace for UNESCO and becoming a spokesperson for their Slave Route Project.

Marcus's new role resulted in a new album in 2015, *Afrodeezia*, written in part to help raise awareness in young people about the history of slavery. Recorded at a variety of studios around the world, Marcus collaborated with musicians from West Africa, South America and the Caribbean to create songs that celebrated the music of African slaves who had, in his words, 'figured out a way to turn their pain and suffering into amazing sounds: spirituals, blues, jazz, R&B.' The album is notable for both Miller's bass work and the adaptation of traditional African musical styles and instruments into his music: album opener 'Hylife' references West African highlife music, underpinned by Marcus's inimitable slap grooves, while on 'B's River' he plays the melody on a gimbri, an African instrument considered to be a distant ancestor of the bass guitar. Following the release of *Afrodeezia*, Marcus embarked on a global tour in support of the album.

# MARCUS MILLER
## GEAR BREAKDOWN

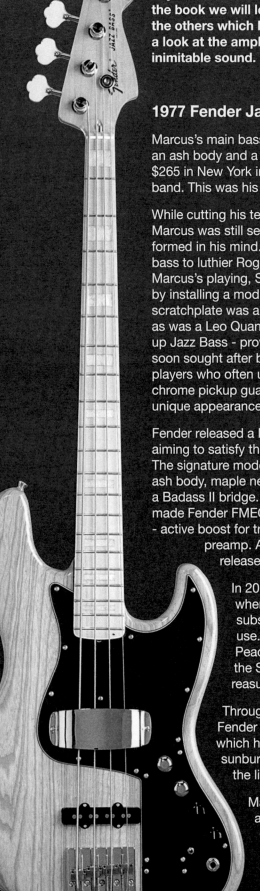

**Unlike other bass players, many of whom change instruments quite regularly, Marcus Miller has forged the majority of his career with one key instrument - his modified 1977 Fender Jazz bass. In this part of the book we will look at this instrument in detail, as well as some of the others which Marcus has used on key recordings. We'll also take a look at the amplification and strings that go towards creating his inimitable sound.**

### 1977 Fender Jazz Bass

Marcus's main bass is a 1977 Fender Jazz (pictured opposite), which has an ash body and a maple fingerboard. He purchased this instrument new for $265 in New York in 1977 during the time he was working in Lenny White's band. This was his third Jazz bass, the previous two having been lost.

While cutting his teeth on the New York session scene in the late seventies, Marcus was still searching for his own sound, an idea of which he had half-formed in his mind. This sound would not be fully realised until he took his bass to luthier Roger Sadowsky for a set-up in 1979: taking an interest in Marcus's playing, Sadowsky helped him to find the sound he was looking for by installing a modified Bartolini TCT preamp in his bass. A new, extended scratchplate was also fitted to cover the additional routing for the preamp, as was a Leo Quan Badass II bridge. The resulting tone - that of a pumped-up Jazz Bass - proved to be exactly what Marcus was looking for and was soon sought after by bass players everywhere. Note that unlike most bass players who often use the slap technique, Marcus decided to leave the chrome pickup guard in place over the neck pickup, adding to the bass's unique appearance.

Fender released a Marcus Miller Signature Jazz Bass in the late nineties, aiming to satisfy the many bassists hungry for the classic Miller tone. The signature model sported most of the same features as Marcus's original: ash body, maple neck and fingerboard, mother-of-pearl block inlays and a Badass II bridge. In place of the modified Bartolini circuit was a custom-made Fender FMEQ active preamp with the same control set as the Bartolini - active boost for treble and bass - as well as a toggle switch to bypass the preamp. A 5-string version of the Marcus Miller Signature Bass was released in 2003.

In 2011 Marcus decided to stop using this original Jazz Bass when touring. Seeking to find suitable replacements, he subsequently purchased several vintage Jazz Basses for live use. In 2013, after beginning work as a UNESCO Artist for Peace, he decided to sell ten of his basses to raise money for the Slave Route Project that he had embarked on and which reasulted in his 2015 album *Afrodeezia*.

Throughout his career, Marcus has used several other notable Fender Jazz basses. He often uses a mid-sixties instrument which has been converted to a lined fretless. This bass has a sunburst finish and rosewood fingerboard and can be seen on the live DVD from the *Tutu Revisited* album.

Marcus also regularly uses a Fodera Emperor 5-string bass and a Modulus Graphite 6-string fretless (heard on 'True Gemini's' from *Tales*). On his 2015 *Afrodeezia* album he also used a 2014 Music Man Sterling Fretless with a piezo pickup.

## Sire Signature Basses

In 2015 Marcus was approached by Sire, a Korean company seeking his input on their new range of bass guitars. Impressed by their ability to build quality instruments at a low price point - something that he was keen to promote for the benefit of young musicians - Marcus agreed to work with them to create a new signature model bass that would be both highly playable and affordable. His modifications included specifying a C-profile

**ABOVE: Marcus with one of his new signature Sire V7 basses**

Two models were released: the V7 and the M3. The V7 is a Jazz-style instrument, available in two configurations: swamp ash with a maple neck and fingerboard, or North American alder with a maple neck and rosewood fingerboard. The M3 is a more modern-looking instrument with two Music Man-style soapbar pickups with exposed pole pieces. Both instruments feature the same electronics - the Marcus Heritage 3-band preamp with sweepable mid control.

The Sire basses - advertised as a 'Game Changer' by the company - proved a big hit upon release, selling out quickly.

**A Sire V7
5-String Bass**

## Strings

Throughout the nineties Marcus favoured DR Hi Beams, gauge .045 - .105. DR manufactured a popular Marcus Miller signature set of strings for many years. In 2015, Marcus began using Dunlop Super Brights, a string which has proved extremely popular with slap players. Dunlop have also released a Marcus Miller signature set.

## Amplification

Over the years Marcus has used a few different setups. He favoured SWR throughout the nineties and early 2000's, often pairing an Interstellar Overdrive Preamp into two SM-900 power amps. For cabinets, he used SWR Goliath III cabs. During his time SWR he also had one of their popular Redhead combos for smaller gigs. In 2006 SWR built a Marcus Miller signature 2-channel preamp.

During the early 2000's Marcus began using EBS equipment, which he continues to use. He favours either the HD350 or HD650 amplifiers paired with two ProLine 4x10 cabinets.

# MARCUS MILLER
## STYLE ANALYSIS

Throughout his long and varied career Marcus Miller has found himself in a huge variety of musical situations, including pop/R&B sessions, TV shows, working as a sideman to jazz/fusion icons, backing up legendary vocalists and playing in front of a symphony orchestra. With such a wide body of work, it's little surprise that he has developed a wide palette of sounds and techniques that can be called forth to suit any situation. In this section of the book we will cover some of the most important aspects of the Miller sound.

In an article covering 'sound' and 'playing style', it's undeniably difficult to do justice to a musician like Marcus Miller. His prowess as a multi-instrumentalist means that not only does he excel at the bass guitar, but also upright and fretless basses too, not to mention his skills as a vocalist, pianist or with the bass clarinet. This article will therefore cover only the elements of his technique that are relevant to his fretted electric bass playing, since that is the focus of the songs transcribed in this book.

### Fingerstyle Playing

Although he is best known for his slap playing, Marcus does of course possess exemplary conventional fingerstyle technique. He plucks with the first two fingers of his picking hand, alternating as appropriate. Like most experienced studio players, he uses different picking hand positions in order to coax a wide variety of tones from the instrument. The two main positions he uses are shown in the photographs below:

**Playing over the bridge pickup**

**'Hard plucking' close to the neck**

For groove playing (and often when playing fretless) he plucks the strings **behind** the chrome pickup cover on his bass, his hand positioned over the bridge pickup - this is shown in the first photograph above. This is a common place to site the hand for playing fingerstyle and results in a tighter tone, with more mid-range bite.

(Note: audio examples are available for all of the exercises in this section. To download them, visit www.basslinepublishing.com and log in to your account. Click Free Stuff on the main menu - you'll find the audio files in a zip folder listed with the bonus content for this book).

## EXERCISE 1

This is a typical Marcus Miller-style groove. If your instrument allows it, solo the bridge pickup and play the line with your picking hand back close to the bridge. Aim for the tight punchy sound you hear on the audio track.

♩ = 95

3

When soloing, Marcus often repositions his picking hand to be **in front** of the pickup cover, much closer to the neck. This is likely something that he picked up from Stanley Clarke, one of his key influences. As the strings are slacker at this point, it's possible to pluck harder, resulting in more 'snap' from the strings. When playing solo lines using this technique, the sound actually approaches that of the slap technique, meaning that the casual listener will be hard-pressed to tell whether he is slapping or playing fingerstyle. Marcus often refers to this style of fingerstyle playing as 'hard plucking'. You can hear some great examples of this on his cover of the Billy Cobham classic 'Red Baron' on the $M^2$ album. Another good example is his solo on 'Boomerang' from the *Master Of All Trades* DVD.

## EXERCISE 2

This is a solo line that is similar to kind of thing that Marcus often plays in his solos. Hard pluck this one with the picking hand close to the end of the neck, and don't be afraid to really dig in.

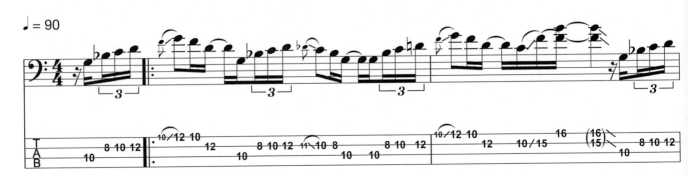

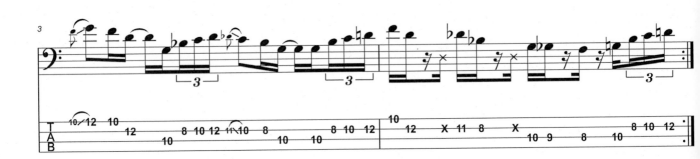

This exercise used the minor pentatonic scale heavily, with some hints of the blues scale too. Both are very commonly used in funk playing and Marcus uses them frequently when soloing in this style.

## Palm Muting

Like many bassists who often play funk, Marcus has developed a very effective palm muting technique. As you'll see from the photograph on the next page, this is performed by resting the fleshy part of the palm of the picking hand across the strings down by the bridge. This acts as a mute and you can of course control the amount of muting that is applied by varying the amount of pressure that you use. The strings are then plucked by the edge of the thumb and if required, the first (and occasionally second) fingers. When palm muting, Marcus uses his thumb for the majority of the time, using the first finger only if the line is too quick to be played with the thumb alone, or if accents on other strings are required. Although simple in principle, this can be a tough technique to get right - the main problem is controlling the level of muting from string to string. You'll find that if you shift to higher strings, you will need to reposition your hand and apply less muting. When using this technique it's quite common to play lines that utilise only two strings.

You can hear some great examples of Marcus using this technique in 'Red Baron', 'Cee-Tee-Eye', 'Jekyll & Hyde', '3 Deuces' and 'Redemption'. A great example can also be seen on the live DVD *Master Of All Trades* during the performance of the Miles Davis classic 'So What', where Marcus uses the technique to perform the famous bass melody.

## EXERCISE 3

Here's an example of a Marcus Miller-style palm muted line. Again, note the use of minor pentatonic and blues scales.

♩ = 85

### Slap Technique

Marcus possesses an extremely comprehensive command of the slap technique, refined through his extensive studio experience in the late seventies. He typically slaps with his thumb in front of the chrome pickup cover on his bass, close to the end of the neck. An interesting point to note regarding Marcus's slap technique is that his thumb does a lot of the work: whereas other bass players might employ fretting hand slaps, hammer-ons or pull-offs to lessen the amount of notes that the thumb needs to play, Marcus does not. A good example of this is the song 'Redemption' from the *Renaissance* album: the main bass groove is a semiquaver-based line that is quite relentless. Marcus slaps each note individually despite there being ample opportunities to use hammer-ons, pull-offs or even double thumbing. However, in doing so, he ensures that each note has the same level of attack, making for a punchier sound. This, in my opinion, is one of the more difficult aspects of Marcus's slap playing to master.

You can hear further examples of Marcus's thumb-heavy lines during the middle section of 'Blast' (beginning at 3:02) and the riff in 'Frankenstein' (at 3:24).

Let's have a look at some lines which will help you focus on this technique.

### EXERCISE 4

This line is similar to line Marcus plays during 'Blast'.

## EXERCISE 5

This exercise is similar to the minor pentatonic riff from 'Frankenstein'.

## Rhythmic Ghosting

Marcus often uses rapid flurries of slapped and popped ghost notes in his basslines and solos. He has sometimes compared this rhythmic element of his playing to the ghosting that a jazz drummer might do on the snare drum between beats. Good examples of this can be heard in the main riff from 'Detroit' (see bar 5 in the transcription later in the book), the bass solo in 'Panther' (at 3:41), the solo in 'Scoop' (at 3:08) and the solo in 'Frankenstein' (at 4:14).

## EXERCISE 6

Here's an example of a bass groove that employs this technique.

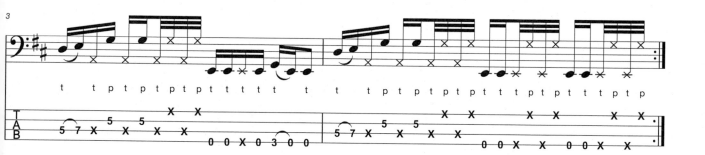

### Double Thumbing

Like many of the more advanced slap players, Marcus also uses the double thumbing technique. This is where the thumb is used in an up-down motion in the same way that one might use a plectrum. This is no doubt the influence of legendary slap pioneer Larry Graham, who used the technique in his work with Sly & The Family Stone and Graham Central Station. The double thumbing technique has of course been widely popularised in the last twenty years by Victor Wooten and Marcus has also acknowledged Victor's work with the technique as an inspiration as well. A great example of Marcus using double thumbing technique can be heard on 'What is Hip' from *Marcus*, where he uses it to perform Rocco Prestia's famous fingerstyle funk groove. You can also hear him use it during the solo on 'Detroit' (see bars 78-79 in the transcription later in the book).

### EXERCISE 7

Here's an example of a Marcus Miller-style double thumbing line. This is similar to Marcus' part in 'What is Hip'.

---

**TIP!**

*When double thumbing you'll need to use a different part of the thumb. Whereas conventional slap technique is typically performed with the edge of the knuckle bone, double thumbing is usually done with the upper corner of the thumb, which must go 'through' the string in order to be able to come back upwards for the upstroke. For more information on double thumbing and other alternative slap techniques, be sure to check out* Ultimate Slap Bass, *also available from Bassline Publishing.*

## Other Classic Marcus Licks

Like all musicians, Marcus has many commonly used licks up his sleeve that can be pulled out on the right occasion. One of his best-known is the descending lick shown in the exercises below. You will hear Marcus use this line often in his basslines and solos and great examples can be heard in 'Bruce Lee', 'Blast', 'Power' and 'Run for Cover'.

## EXERCISE 8

This is an example of Marcus's classic descending slap lick. The thumb does not need to work hard in this lick as Marcus uses pull-offs and slides extensively.

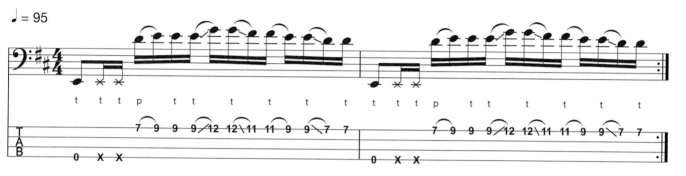

## EXERCISE 9

Here's a commonly used variation on the previous lick. Here, Marcus frets the notes an octave below as well to thicken up the sound and strums the riff.

### Triplets

Triplets are a popular rhythmic device for many slap bassists and Marcus is no exception. However, those who have studied Marcus's work in detail will have discovered that he has a wide variety of ways in which he incorporates triplets into his slap playing. Let's look at a few examples of this.

### EXERCISE 10

This first triplet exercise is performed by slapping with the thumb then following this with two popped notes, performed by the first and second fingers of the picking hand respectively.

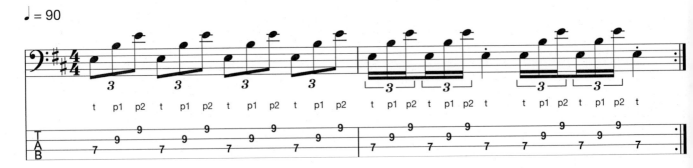

### EXERCISE 11

Here's an exercise that puts this first triplet figure to use in the context of a groove.

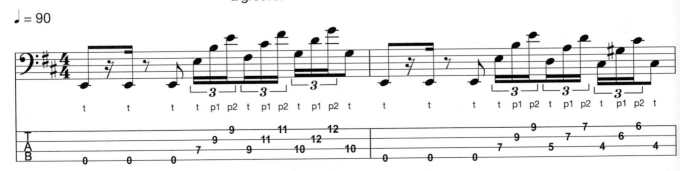

You can hear Marcus use this technique during the Intros of 'Bruce Lee' and 'Boogie On Reggae Woman', both from the *Silver Rain* album.

## EXERCISE 12

This is the same technique described on the previous page, only this time performed as ghost notes. You can hear Marcus use the technique in this way in the main groove of 'Run for Cover'.

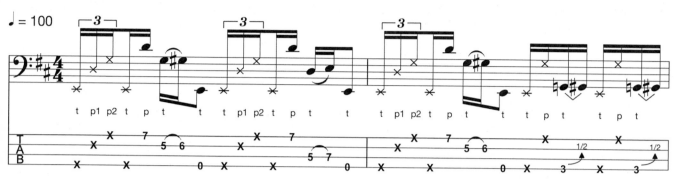

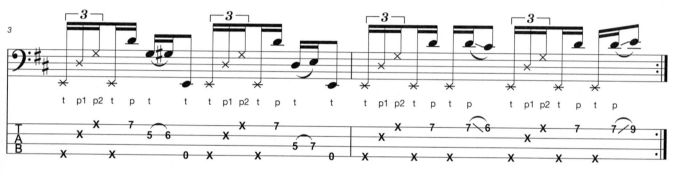

## EXERCISE 13

Marcus also plays triplets using the double thumbing technique. When doing so, he most commonly plays two semiquaver triplets. This is a total of six notes, meaning that the thumb strokes can be down-up-down-up-down-up. This simple exercise will get you started with this technique.

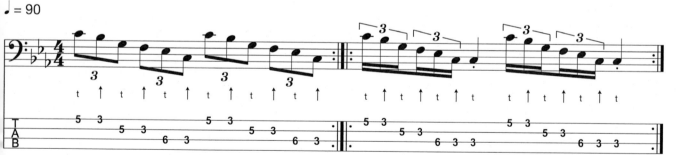

## EXERCISE 14

This example features the double thumbed triplet lick from the previous exercise in the context of a Marcus Miller-inspired line.

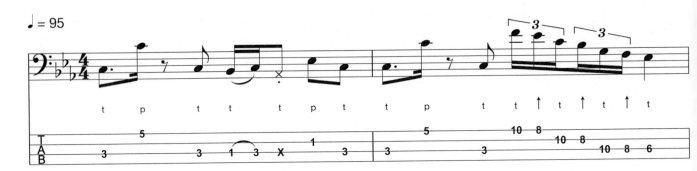

Marcus often uses this technique to play descending pentatonic phrases as heard during the main riffs from 'Power', 'Bruce Lee' and 'Blast'.

## EXERCISE 15

Let's take a look at another triplet figure commonly used by Marcus. In this example, a note is slapped by the thumb, followed by a hammer-on, then followed by a popped note. The popped note is often an open string, or a ghost note.

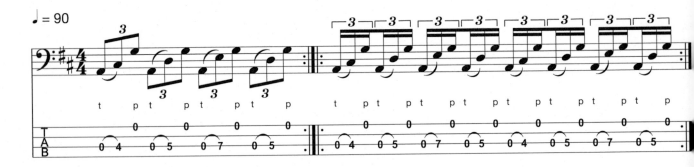

## EXERCISE 16

This triplet figure can sound very effective when used in bass grooves and solos. It allows for rapid flurries of notes, with little effort.

This is quite a simple way to play fast triplets and you can hear Marcus use it during the solos on 'Bruce Lee', 'Cee-Tee-Eye' and 'Lonnie's Lament'.

## EXERCISE 17

A more recent development in Marcus's playing has been the use of the down-up-pop technique to play triplets. To do this, slap the string, allowing your thumb to travel through it as discussed in the double thumbing explanation earlier. Then thumb an upstroke and follow this with a pop. Although this will take some getting used to initially, you should find that you are able to work this up to quite fast tempos.

27

## EXERCISE 18

Now let's use this triplet figure in the context of a bassline.

You can hear Marcus use this technique during his solo on 'Cee-Tee-Eye' (see bars 99 and 101 in the transcription later in the book).

## EXERCISE 19

The following example is a slap bass solo in the style of Marcus Miller. This short piece utilises many of the slap techniques described above.

## Tapping

Unlike fellow virtuoso bassists like Victor Wooten or Billy Sheehan, Marcus is not particularly known for his tapping, although he does have a few techniques that are worth mentioning.

The most common tapping that Marcus uses is a form of legato tapping. This is unique to Marcus in that he uses the edge of the plucking hand thumb to tap notes directly on the fingerboard rather than using the index or middle fingers as other bassists do. He most often uses this in conjunction with rapid hammer-ons and pull-offs from the fretting hand. The hand positions required for this are shown in the photograph below.

**RIGHT: Marcus's 'bass yodelling' tapping technique**

Marcus sometimes refers to this this technique as 'bass yodelling', an example of how his experience with vocalists such as Luther Vandross, Roberta Flack and Lalah Hathaway has informed his phrasing on the bass.

## EXERCISE 20

This exercise will help you work up Marcus's 'bass yodelling' technique. Once you have mastered this at the specified tempo, try doing it as fast as you can - the idea is to build it up to be a flurry of notes.

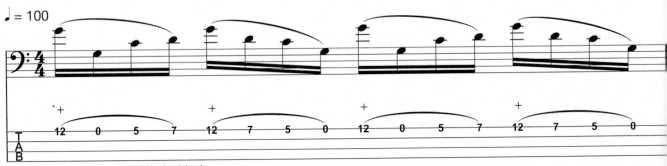

* note is tapped with the edge of the picking hand thumb

This technique can be heard during the intro of 'Bruce Lee'. You can also hear it in 'Lonnie's Lament', 'Scoop', 'Boomerang' and many others.

Marcus also uses a more conventional two handed tapping technique whereby he taps notes with both the fretting hand and plucking hand directly on the fretboard. This is similar to how a piano player would play and can be a very versatile technique.

## EXERCISE 21

This simple tapping exercise demonstrates Marcus's application of the two handed tapping technique.

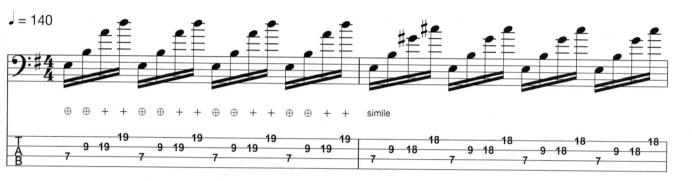

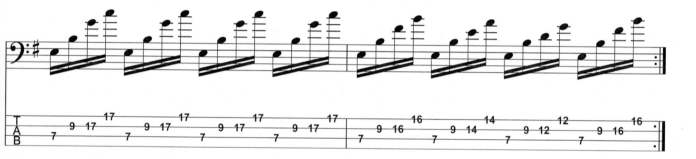

You can hear Marcus employ this technique during the Intro of 'Scoop' and at the end of his bass solo on 'Frankenstein' (at 4:58 on the recording). You can also clearly see Marcus applying this technique during the Intro of 'Scoop' on the *Marcus Miller in Concert* DVD.

Marcus also used the two handed tapping technique in a slower, more compositional manner in his composition 'Mr. Pastorius' from *The Sun Don't Lie.'*

## Artificial Harmonics

Marcus occasionally uses artificial harmonics as decorations in his playing. This is likely to be a Jaco Pastorius influence, who used them on the Intro to the classic Weather Report track 'Birdland'. Marcus performs these in the same way, resting the edge of his thumb on the string an octave above the fretted note, then plucking behind the thumb with his index finger. This is shown in the photograph below.

**RIGHT: Playing artificial harmonics - the thumb creates a node point and the first finger plucks the string**

### EXERCISE 22

This simple line demonstrates the sound of artificial harmonics.

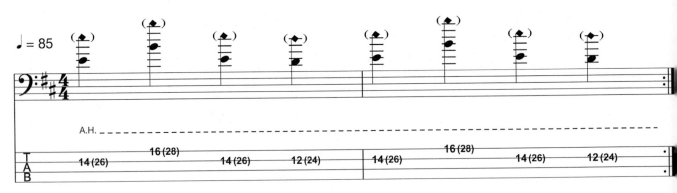

You can hear Marcus use artificial harmonics during the Intro to 'Panther' from *The Sun Don't Lie*.

# MARCUS MILLER
## THE MUSIC

# Detroit

**Written by Marcus Miller**

Funk Rock ♩ = 92

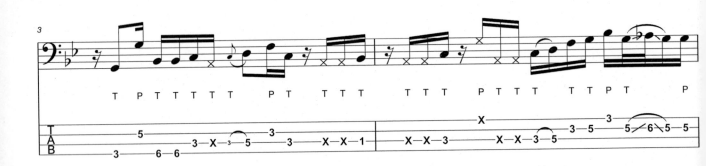

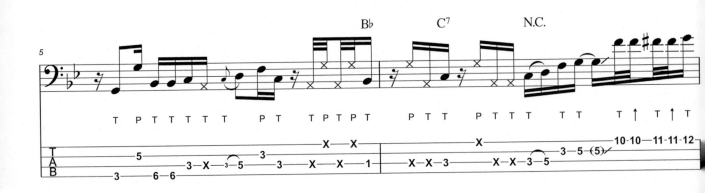

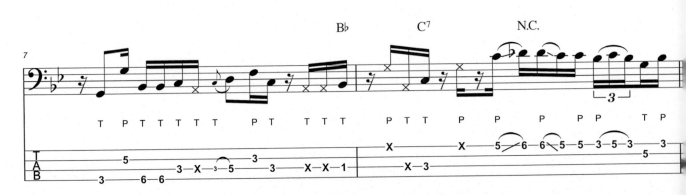

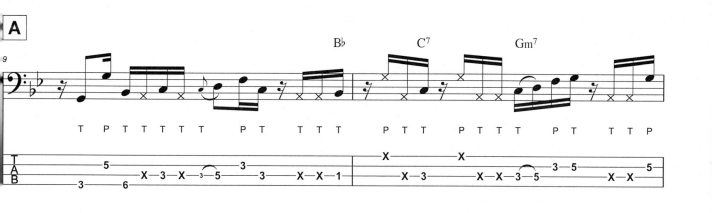

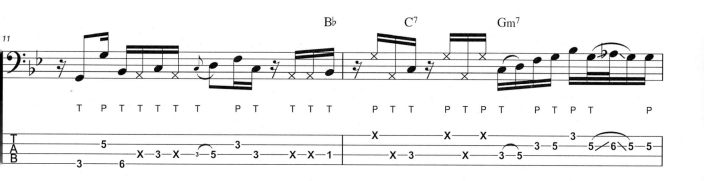

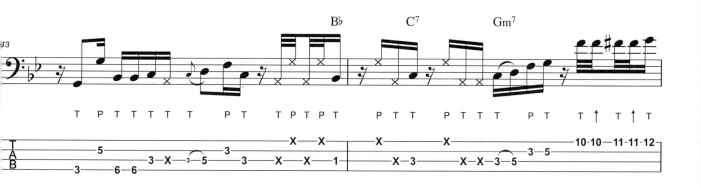

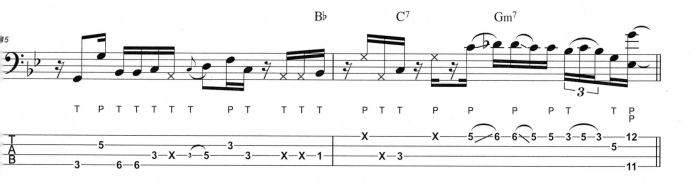

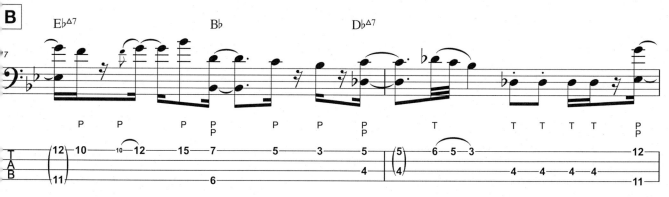

35

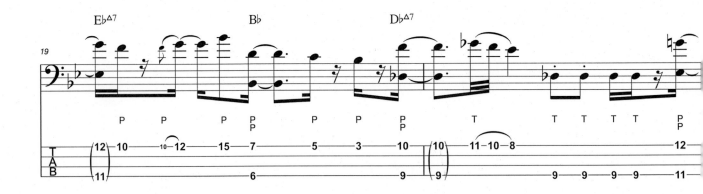

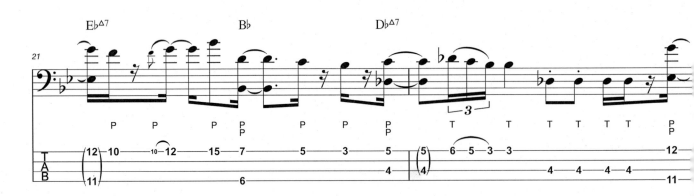

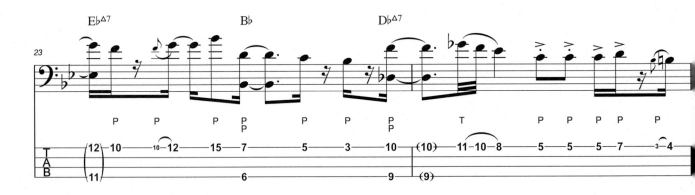

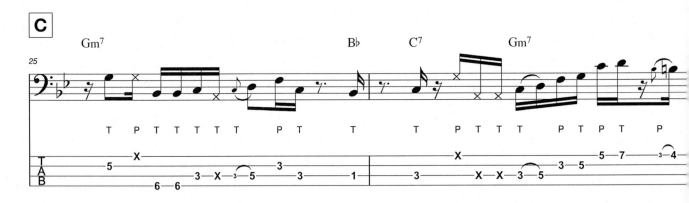

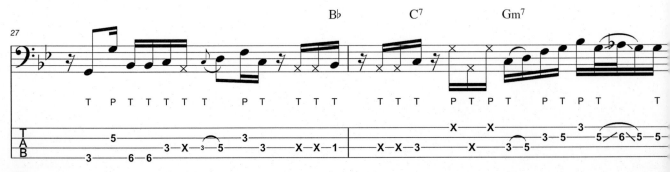

36

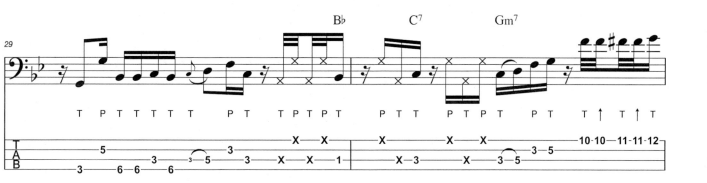

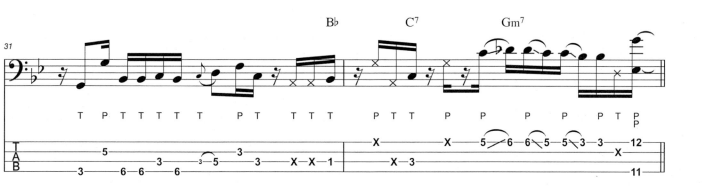

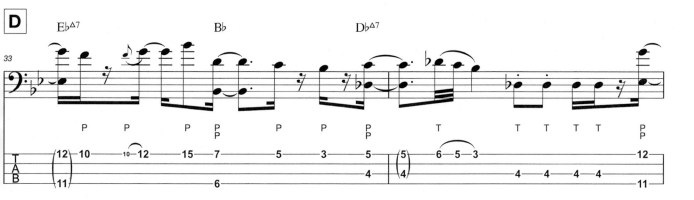

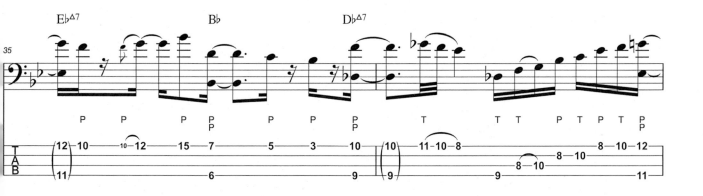

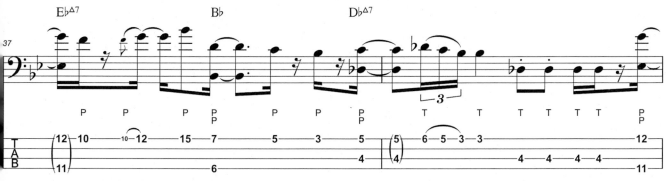

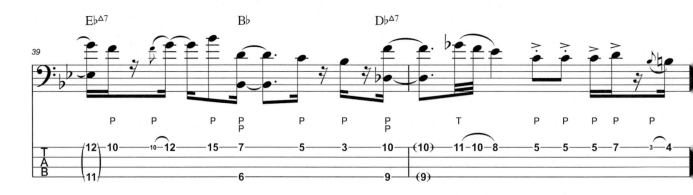
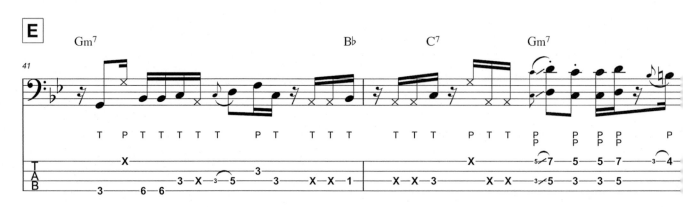
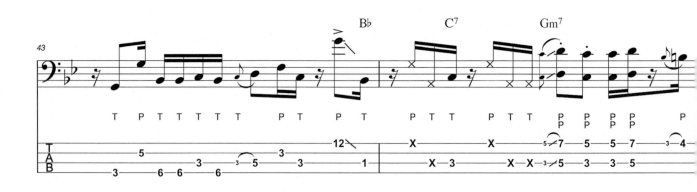
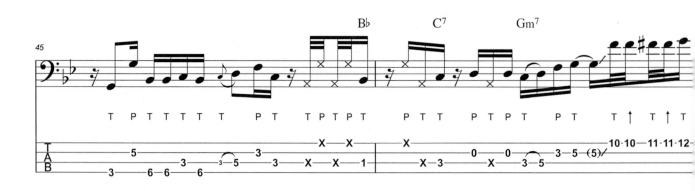
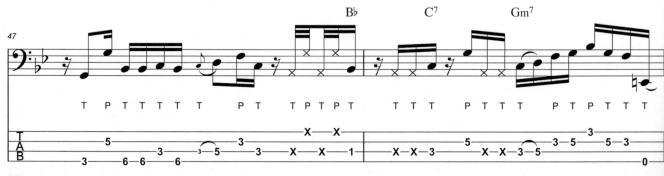

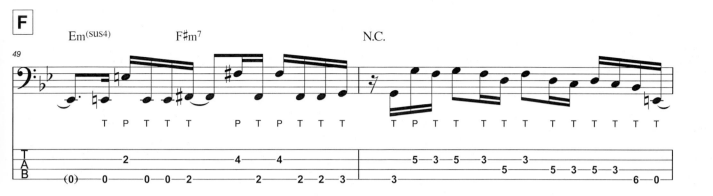

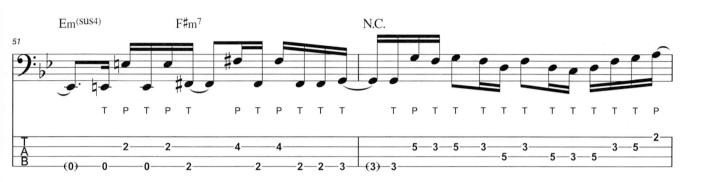

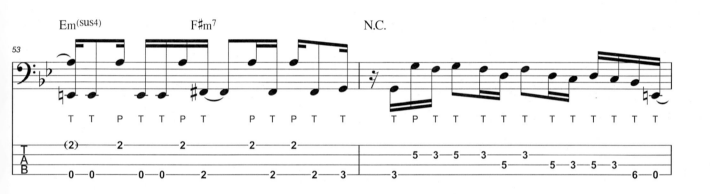

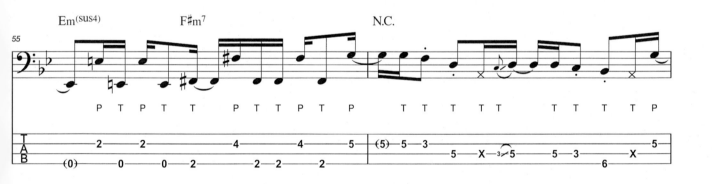

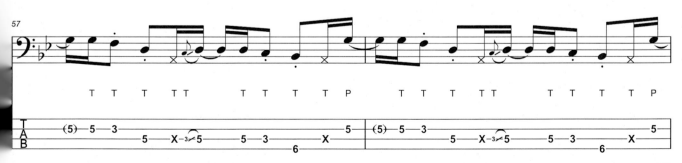

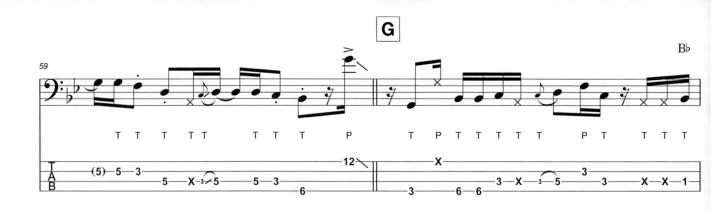

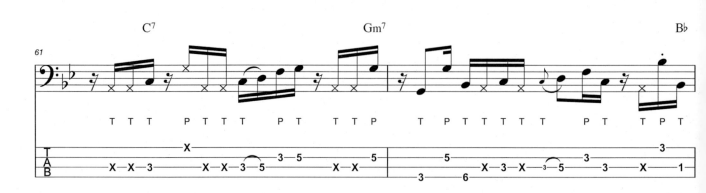

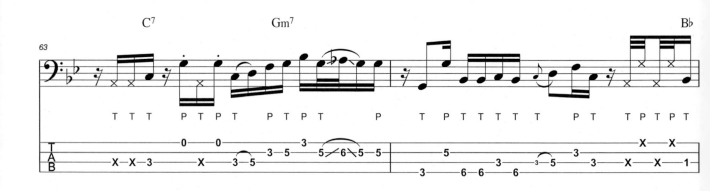

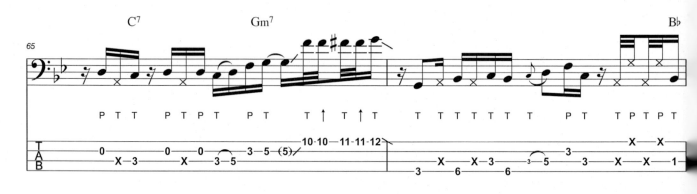

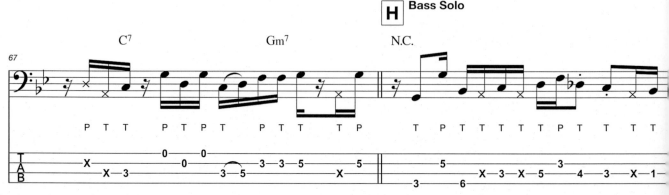

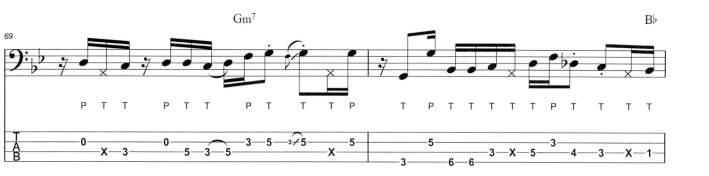
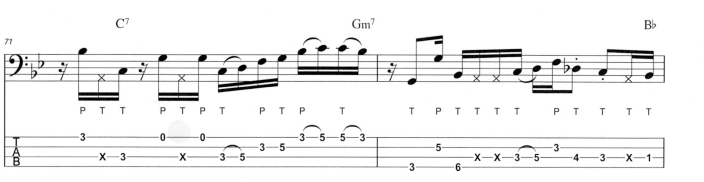
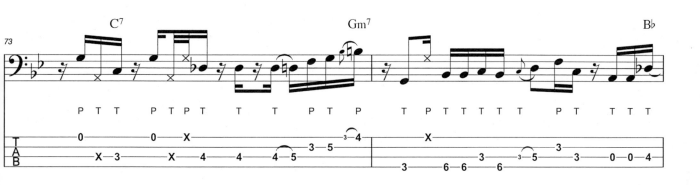
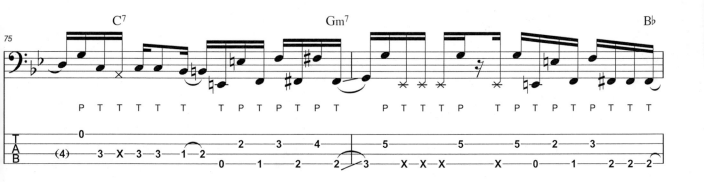
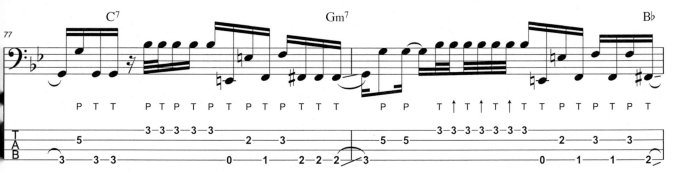

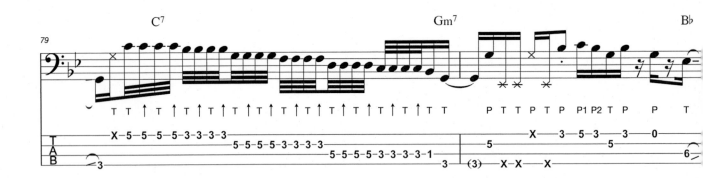

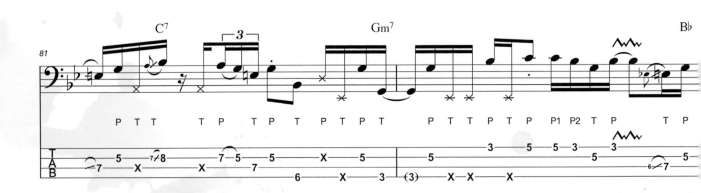

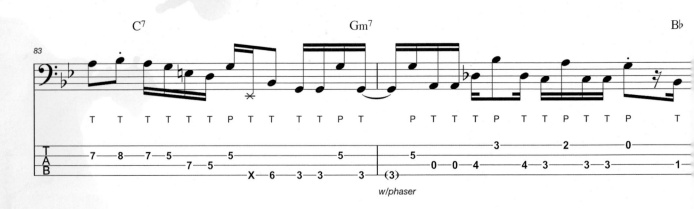

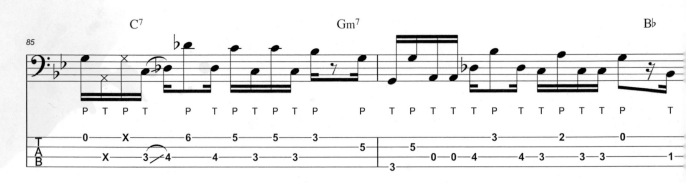

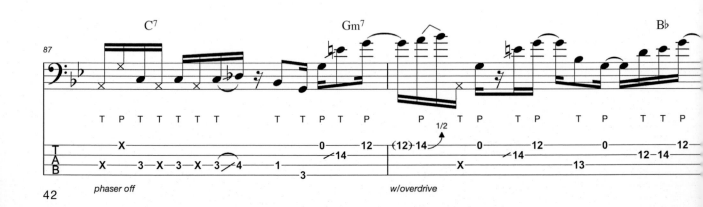

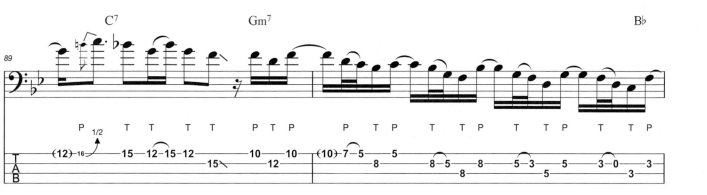

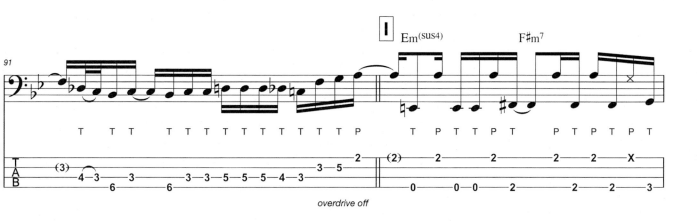

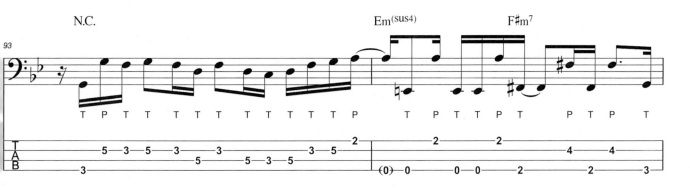

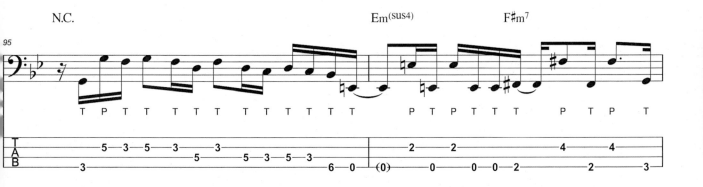

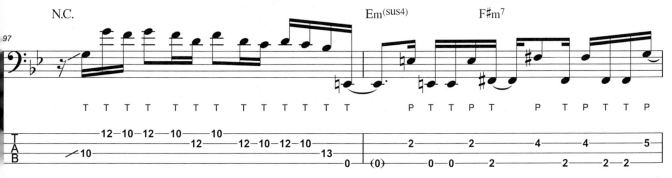

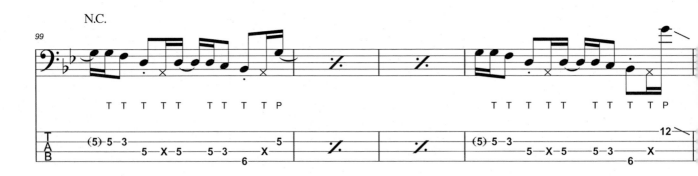

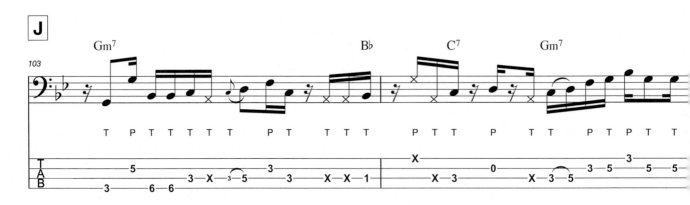

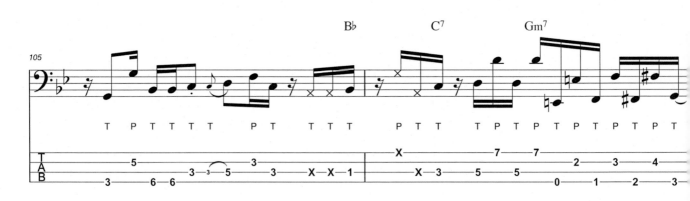

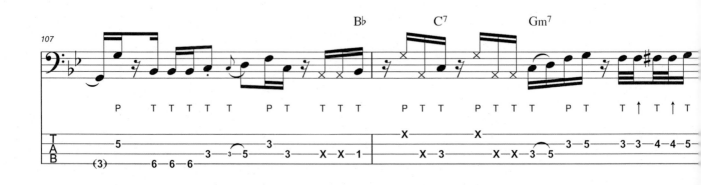

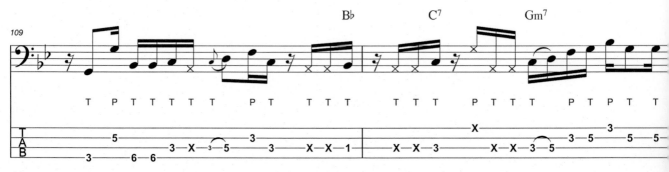

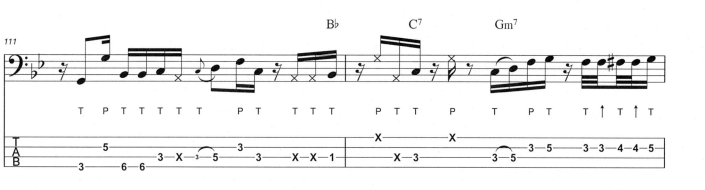
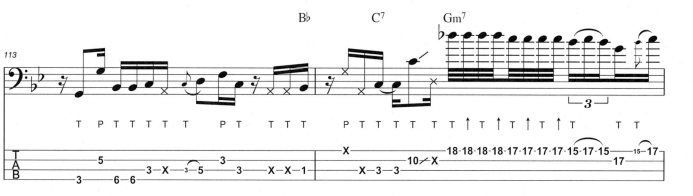
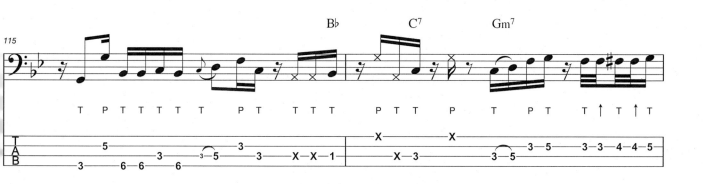
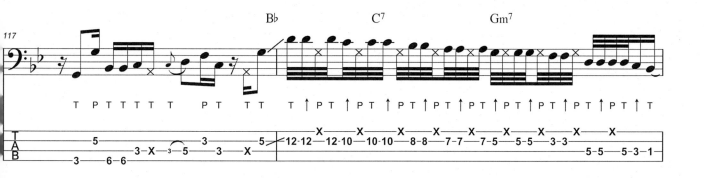
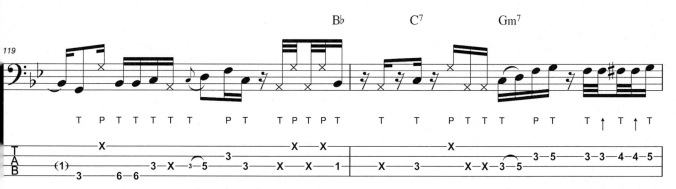

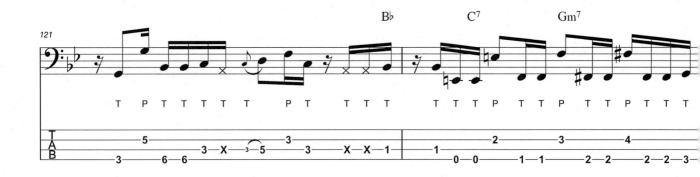
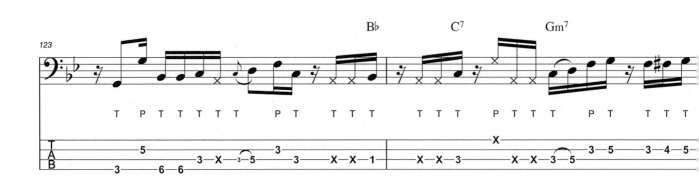
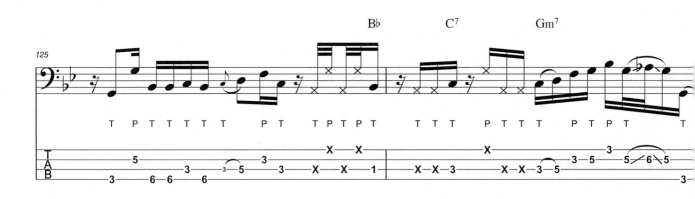
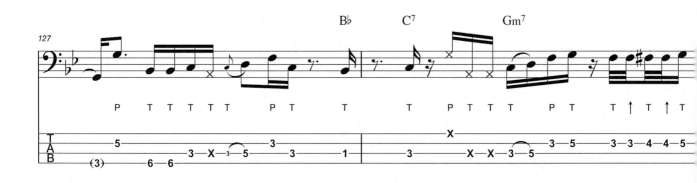
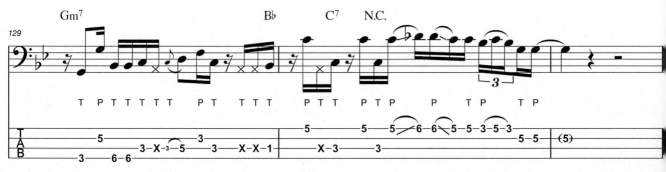

# 'Detroit' - Performance Notes

**'Detroit' is the first track on *Renaissance*. As is typical with Marcus's opening tracks, this piece serves the dual purpose of reminding the listener what Marcus is about, as well as hinting at the direction that the album will take. In this case, Marcus's unique brand of bass-driven funk is front and centre, enhanced through minimal studio production that puts the emphasis on the live energy created by his supremely talented young band.**

'Detroit' is a funk rock tune in G minor that opens with a typically meaty bass riff from Marcus. Although this part is a little simpler than some of Marcus's other well-known grooves, there are nevertheless some potential pitfalls to watch out for. When learning this line, be sure to observe the TAB positions for the B♭ in the first bar: at the beginning of the bar it is played at the sixth fret of the E-string, while at the end of the bar it is played at the first fret of the A-string. This second B♭ falls on the final semiquaver subdivision of the fourth beat and is followed in the second bar by a C played on the same subdivision of the first beat. Playing a note on this heavily syncopated part of the beat is difficult to execute accurately, but is vital to the feel of the line - playing this note early or late will upset the feel considerably. Note that Marcus adds ghost notes before each of these pitched notes - these will help you place the note more accurately, whilst adding some rhythmic interest. You'll notice that this entire groove is peppered with ghost notes, most of which are performed with the thumb. As you'll have seen from the Style Analysis, Marcus uses his thumb a great deal, often eschewing fretting hand slaps and hammer-ons in favour of actual slapped notes. This line is a good example of this aspect of Marcus's slap technique.

The remainder of this groove contains some typical Marcus Miller flourishes: the quick slur from G - A♭ - G at the end of bar 4, the upper register double thumbing lick in bar 6 and the fluid unison line that ends the riff in bar 8. Note that this final riff is played entirely with popped notes and slurs, a great example of the vocal-like phrasing that Marcus is known for.

At Letter B the main melody enters, played by Marcus. This line is played by plucking melody notes with the first finger and lower bass notes with the thumb. For example, at the beginning of bar 17, the low E♭ is plucked by the thumb while the G a tenth higher is plucked by the first finger. When playing this melody take care to play all grace notes as written and follow the notation guide between this staves - this is important because Marcus often slaps notes that others would pop, such as the D♭-C-B♭ slur at the beginning of bar 18. You should also notice that each chord begins on the last semiquaver of the beat - this is a key part of the feel during this section. This part is followed by a return to the main theme.

At letter E we hear the main bass groove again, this time with some small embellishments such as the descending

slide from the upper G in bar 43 and the popped octaves in bar 44. At letter F an interlude section begins: this part consists of relatively simple root-octave popped figures from E and F♯, followed by a descending G minor pentatonic lick. Note that later in the riff (bar 53 for example) the A at the second fret of the G-string is popped over the E minor chord instead of the octave E. The backing chord contains a suspended fourth (A) and Marcus chooses to reflect this in his line here.

Marcus's bass solo begins at letter H and is based around the main bass groove from the beginning of the piece. Note the heavy emphasis on the blue note (D♭) in the opening bars of the solo. As is typical of his solos, Marcus builds the intensity gradually, first adding popped octave licks (bars 75 - 76) then beginning to incorporate flurries of double thumbed notes. These culminate in a long double thumbed descending lick in bar 79. Here, Marcus descends through the G minor pentatonic from C at the fifth fret of the G-string, playing each note four times. In terms of technique, this is relatively simple, requiring only fast down and up strokes with the thumb (see the Style Analysis, page 22 for more on double thumbing).

Marcus incorporates effects into the second half of his solo, something that is a relatively recent addition to his sonic palette. In bar 84 he begins a new lick based on descending sixth intervals played with a phaser - likely to be an MXR Phase 90. He then ends his solo with an upper register lick that is played with a mild overdrive. Marcus has several overdrive pedals in his set-up including an Fulltone OCD and a Rodenburg GAS-MM multi-pedal overdrive unit.

The remainder of the piece consists of repeats of the main groove and the interlude section that was earlier heard at letter F. There are many embellishments added along the way however - check out the upper register double thumbed lick in bar 114 and the descending double thumb and popped lick in bar 118 for example.

Have fun learning this track. As Marcus's music contains a heavy element of improvisation, your ultimate goal should be to improvise your own licks and ideas where you feel they are needed. Studying and learning Marcus's lines before you do this will enable you to incorporate his ideas into your own palette.

# Redemption

**Written by Marcus Miller**

Jazz Funk ♩ = 88

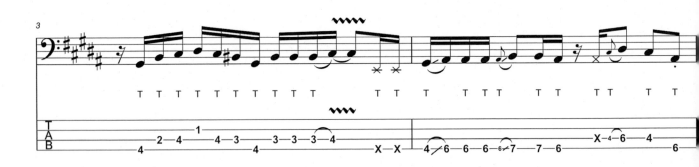

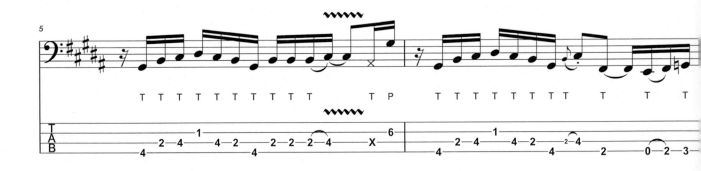

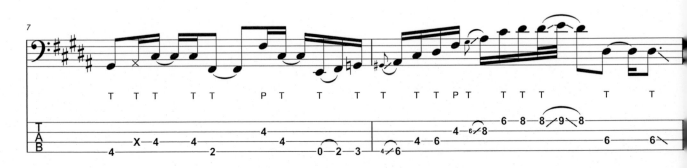

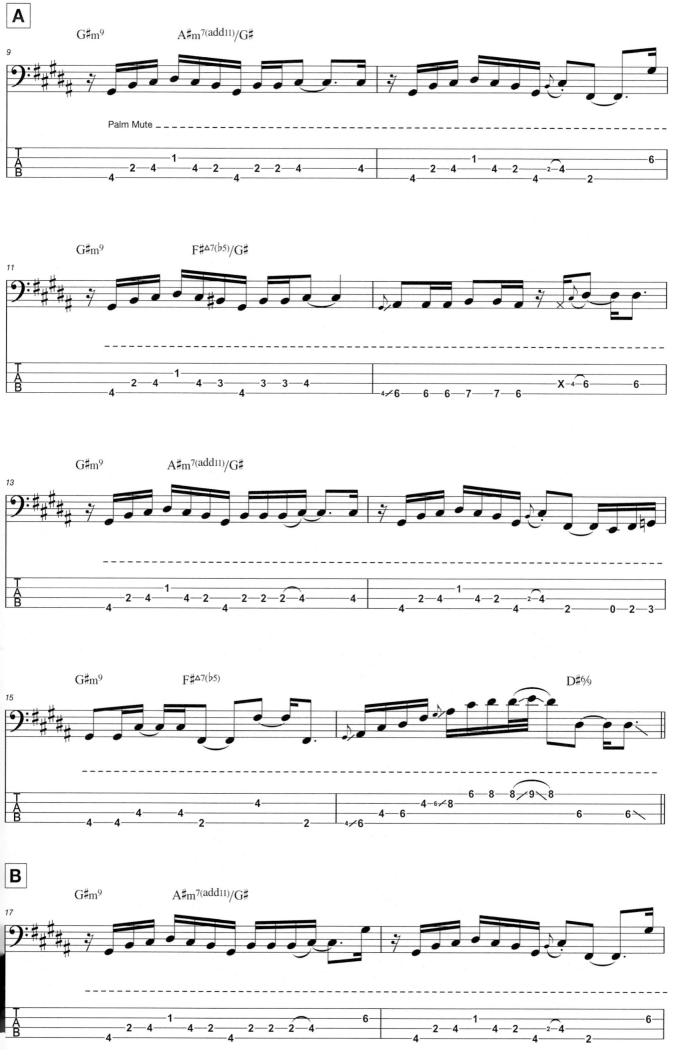

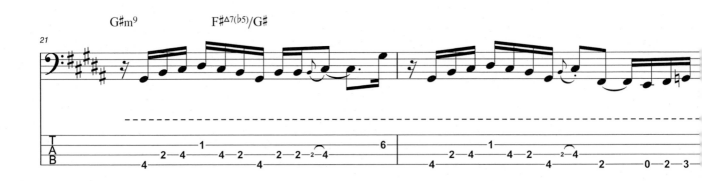

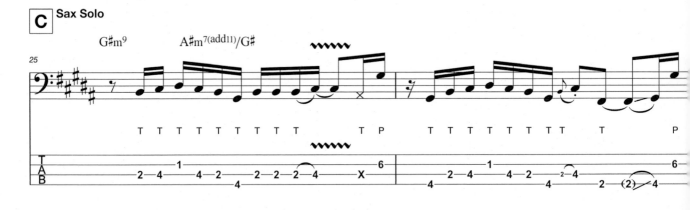

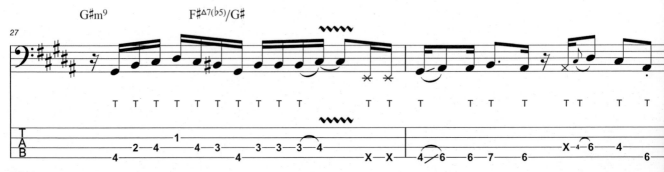

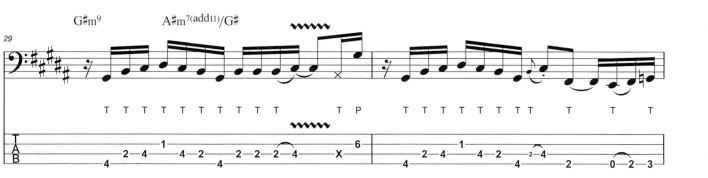

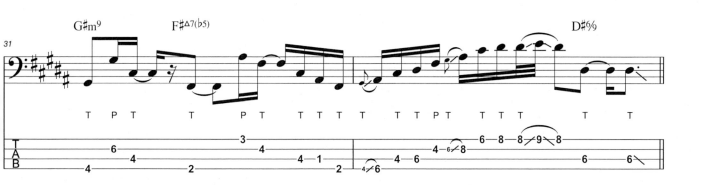

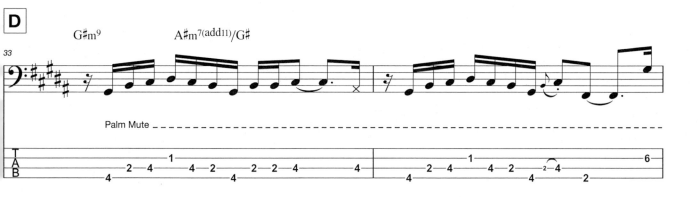

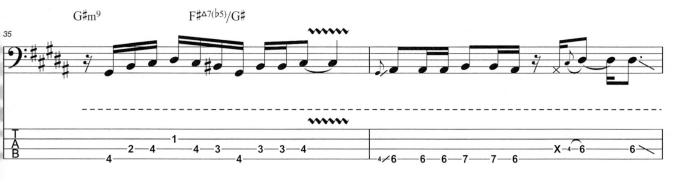

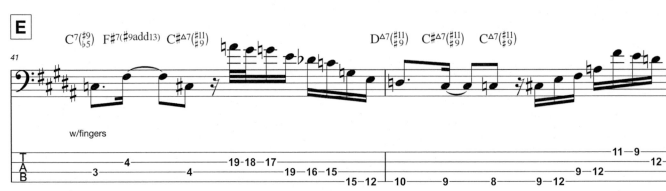

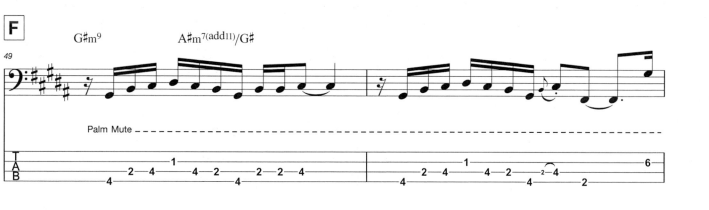

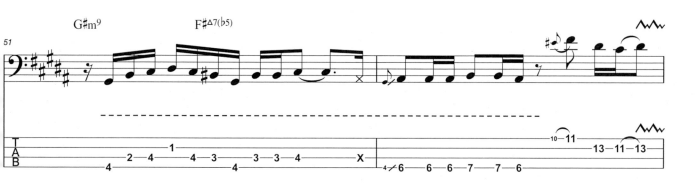

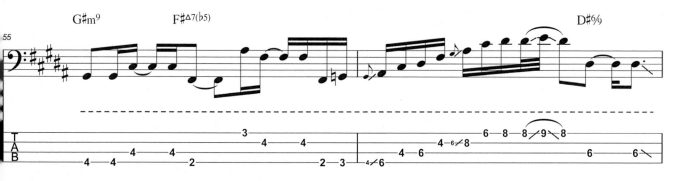

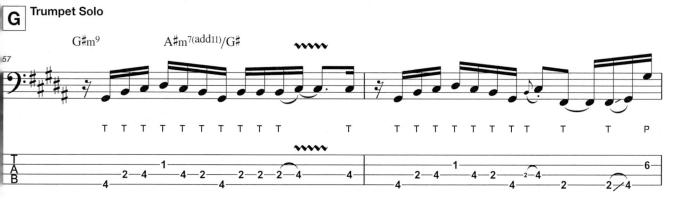

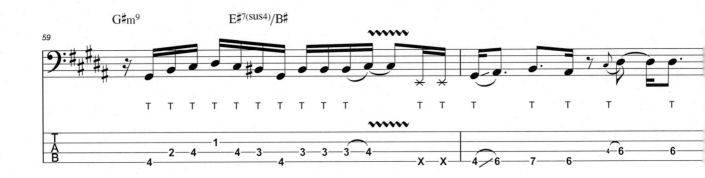

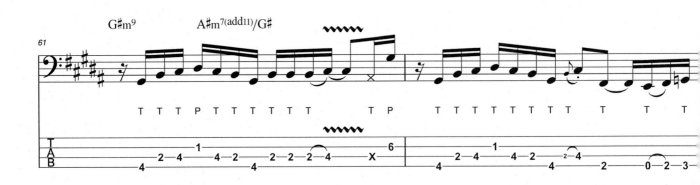

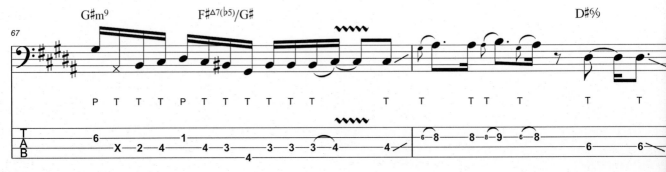

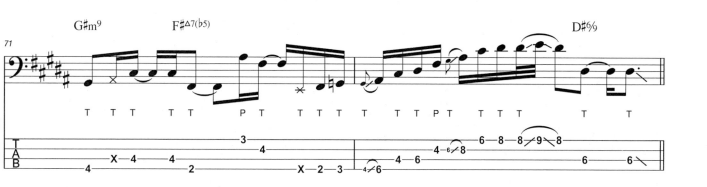

**H** Sax Solo

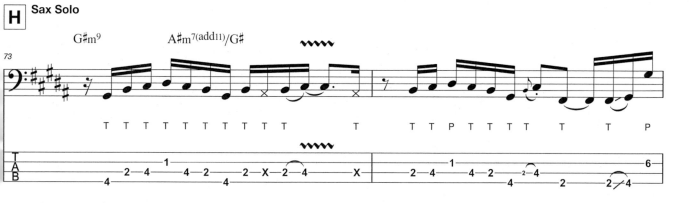

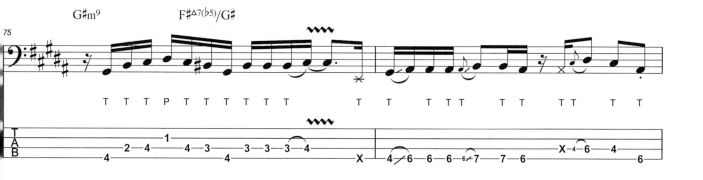

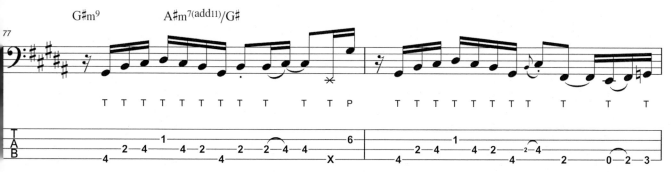

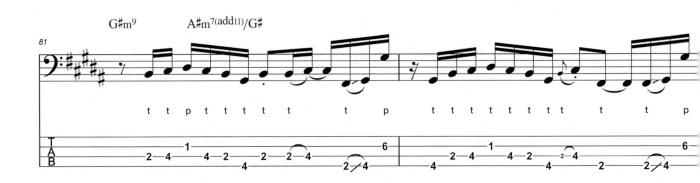

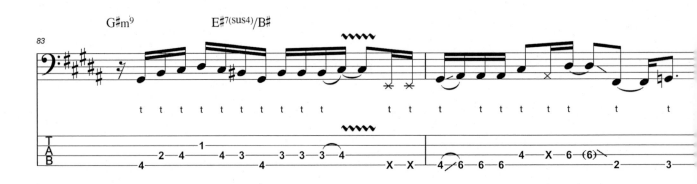

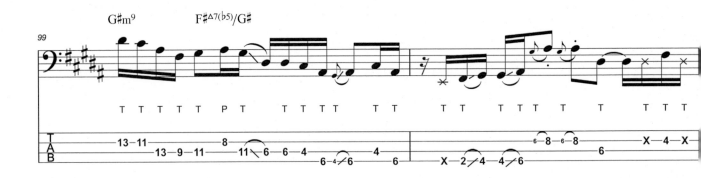

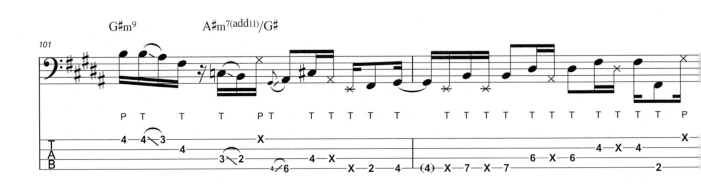

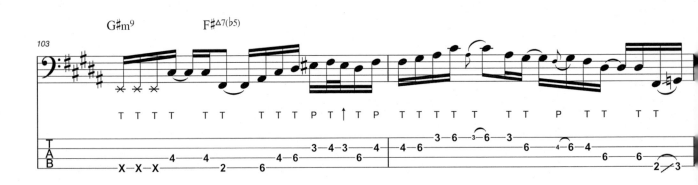

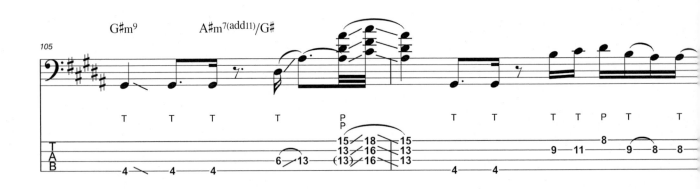

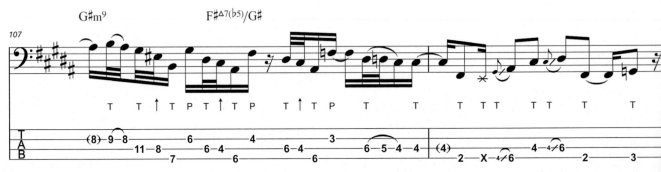

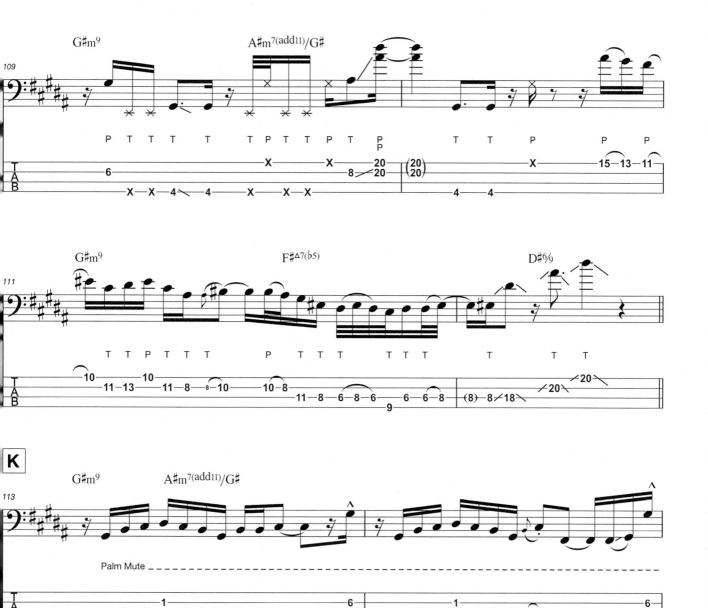

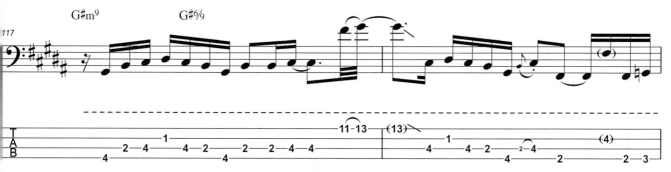

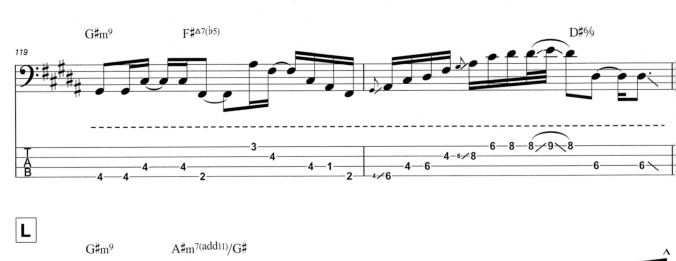

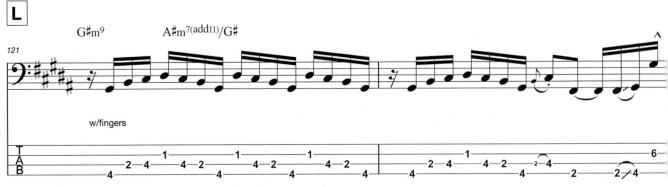

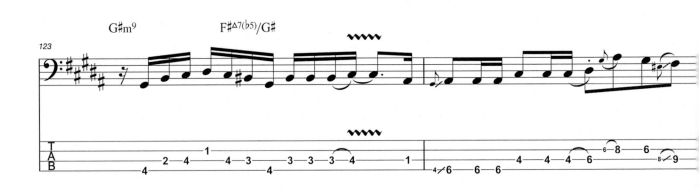

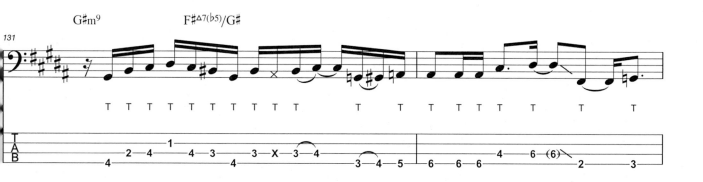

**Fade Out**

# 'Redemption' - Performance Notes

**'Redemption' is the second track on *Renaissance* and has been mentioned by Marcus on several occasions as being a key song in terms of determining the direction the album would take. Featuring a challenging slapped line and a blistering solo, it has everything we've come to expect from a classic Marcus Miller track.**

The song opens with Marcus's slapped bass groove. This is a busy, semiquaver-based line that is played almost entirely with the thumb. Whereas other bassists might have considered using hammer-ons, pops or slides to ease the burden on the thumb, Marcus instead articulates almost every note in this way, only popping occasional accents on the final semiquaver subdivision of the bar. The relatively slow tempo allows for a continuously slapped line such as this, but when working on it, aim to play each note with a consistent level of volume and attack - this is especially important when crossing strings. It's common for notes slapped on the D and G-strings to decay quickly, so take extra care when playing parts such as the final bar of the sequence (bar 8), which requires you to slap several notes on the G-string. Although many slap players favour slightly lighter gauge strings, using a standard set (.045 - .105) as Marcus does will help notes such as these to sound stronger. When playing this line be sure to follow the notation guide written between the staves in order to play the part in the same way that Marcus does.

The eight-bar groove established in the Intro is reused for many other parts of the song. At letter A it is played again, this time with the palm muting technique. You can read more about this technique in the Style Analysis at the beginning of the book, but essentially this is done by resting the edge of the palm of the picking hand across the strings by the bridge and then plucking the strings with the edge of the thumb. The palm acts as a mute, resulting in a dull, muted tone - this is a technique that Marcus uses frequently in his playing.

At letter E a new section begins, featuring a very challenging part from Marcus. This line is played with conventional fingerstyle technique. When learning this part, it might seem more logical to play the descending riff in the first bar starting from the A at the fourteenth fret of the G-string rather than the nineteenth fret of the D-string as shown in the TAB. This is perfectly acceptable, although the TAB reflects the way that Marcus plays the line live.

Marcus's bass solo begins at letter J. He opens the solo with a standard voicing of a $G\#m^7$ chord, playing the root on the E-string, the seventh on the D-string and the minor third on the G-string. He immediately slides the top two notes up an octave and then slides them back and forth chromatically. He follows this opening statement with a melodic phrase which briefly hints at the $G\#$ Dorian mode (thanks to the use of the $E\#$). In bar 105 he plays another upper register chord voicing, this time implying an $A\#m^{7add11}$ chord - the voicing includes a root and octave, with the eleventh in between. This figure slides up a minor third which allows us to hear the minor third of the chord ($C\#$) as well. The descending lick in bar 107 is a challenging one and requires several upstrokes with the thumb in addition to conventional slap technique - Marcus often uses double thumbing for rapid flurries of notes in this way.

The remainder of the song consists of the two parts heard earlier, with the main groove played with the fingerstyle technique at letter L, then slapped at letter M for the Outro. Note some of the cool variations on the line: the repeating semiquaver figure in bar 121 and the descending $F\#$ pentatonic lick in bar 127 for example.

There are several great live versions of this available for viewing on YouTube. In particular, the version from the Java Jazz Festival 2013 is worth watching and features stellar performance from all members of Marcus's band.

# Jekyll & Hyde

**Written by Marcus Miller**

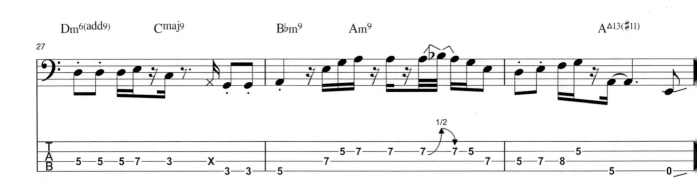

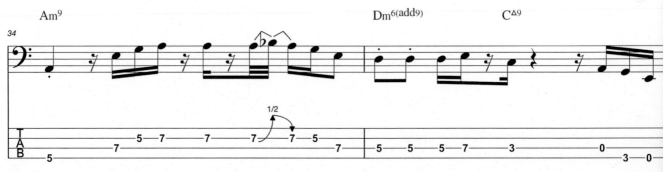

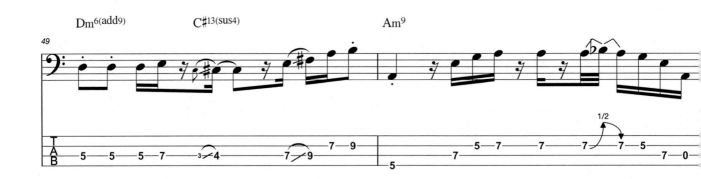

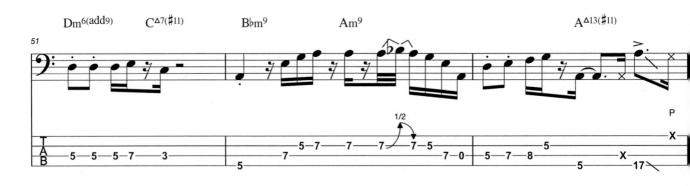

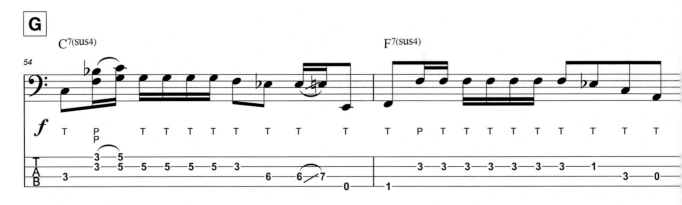

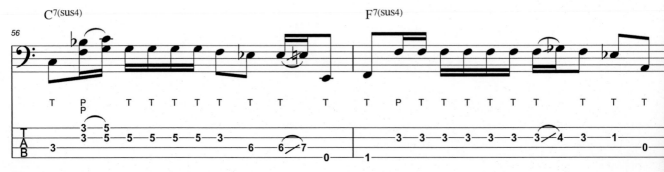

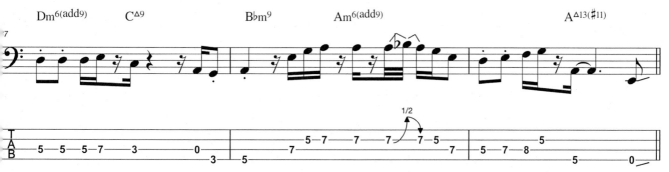

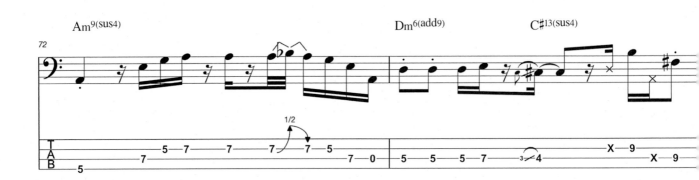

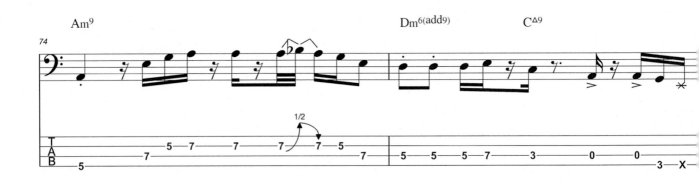

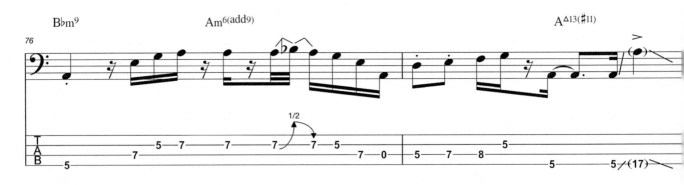

**Guitar Solo**

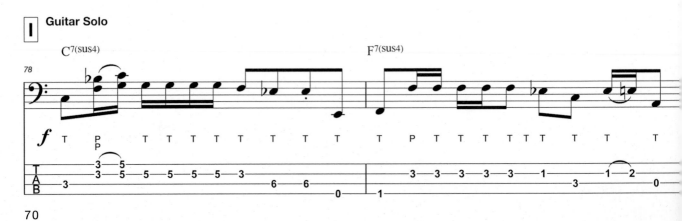

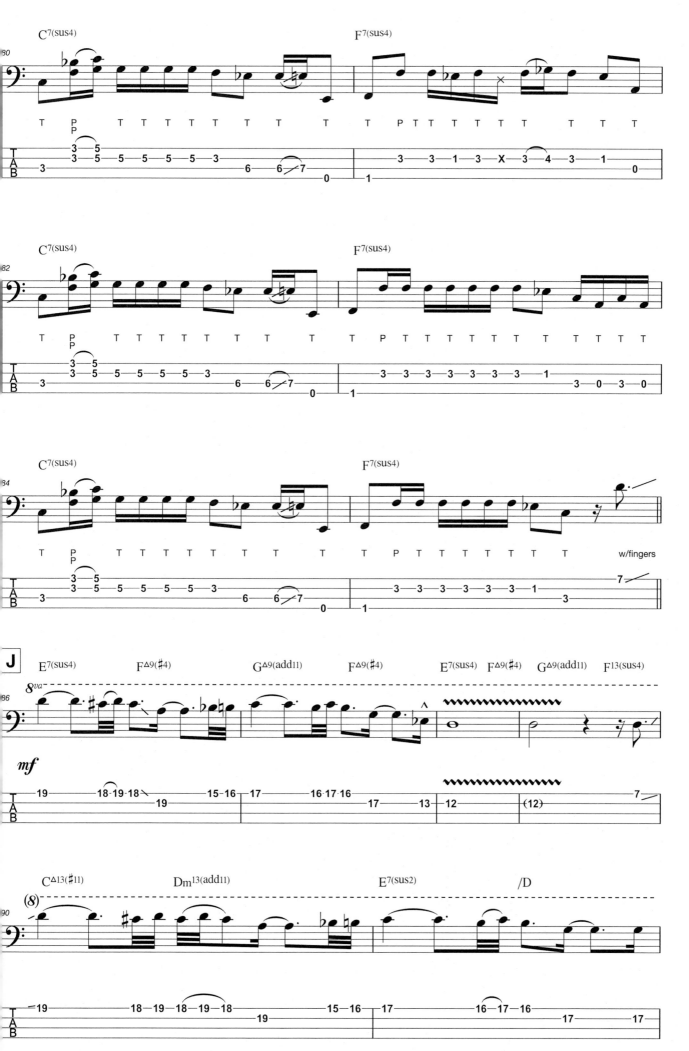

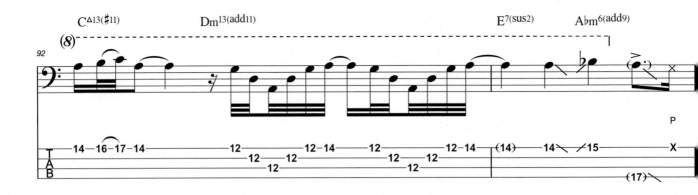

**K** **Organ Solo**

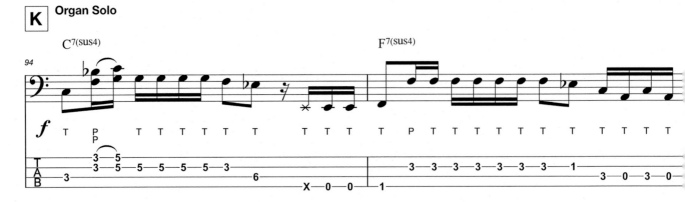

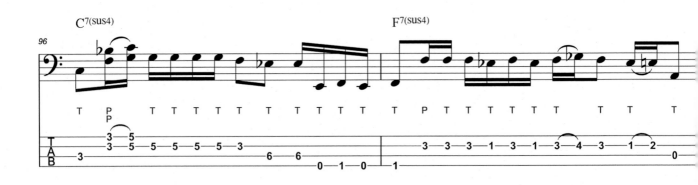

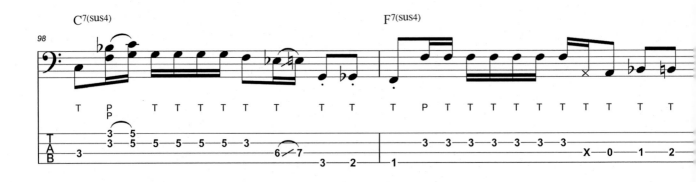

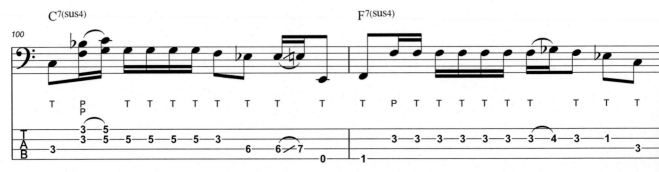

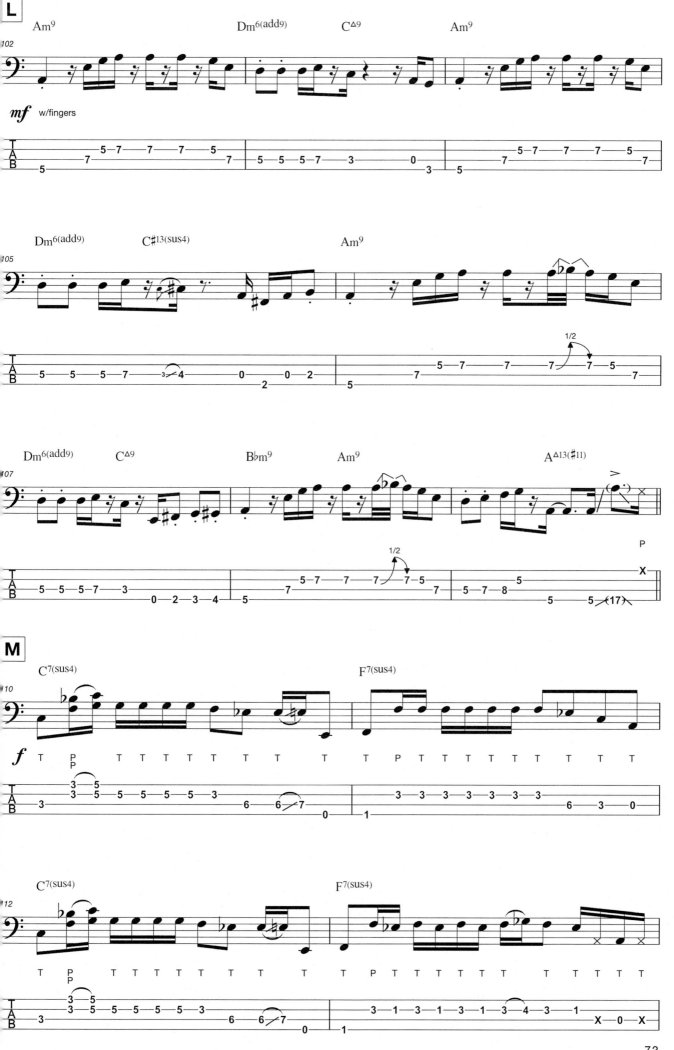

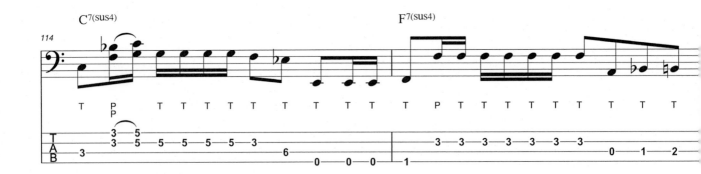

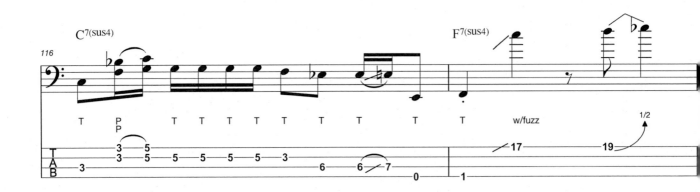

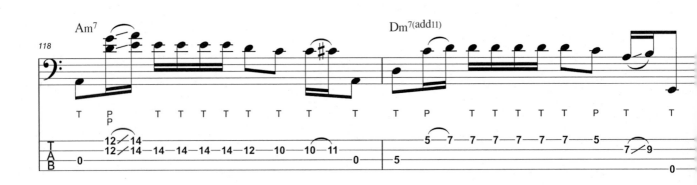

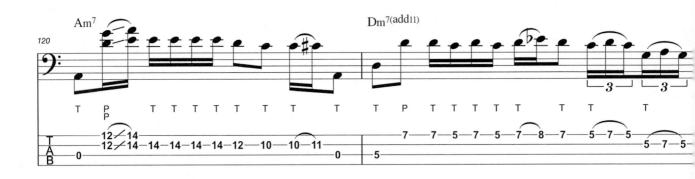

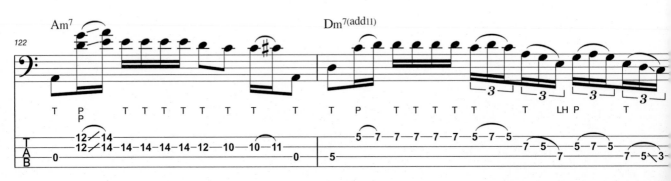

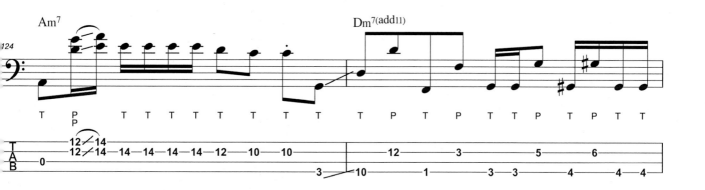

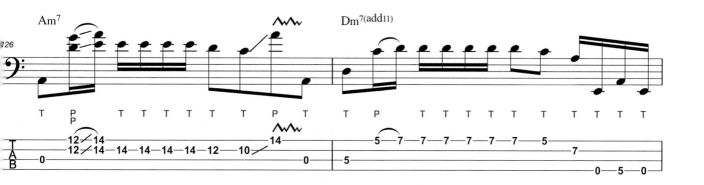

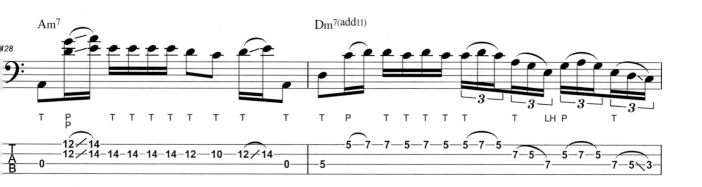

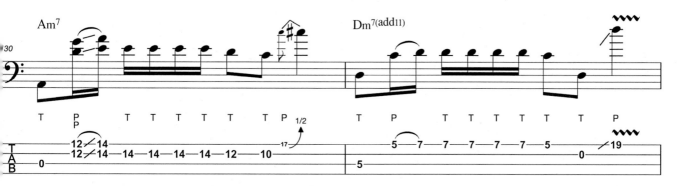

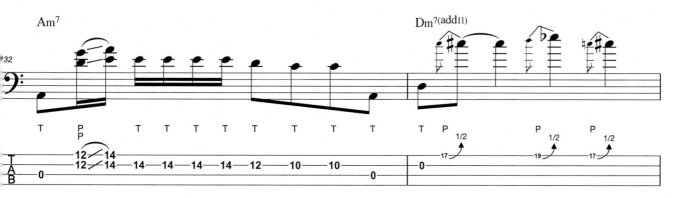

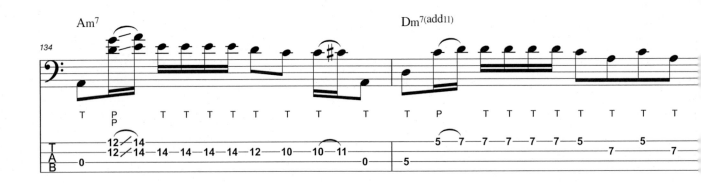

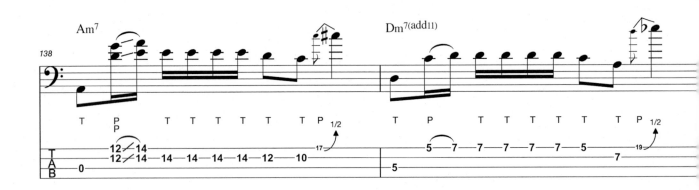

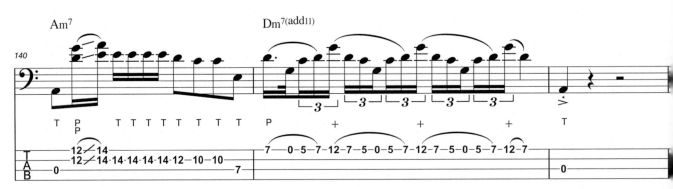

+ = notes are tapped with the edge of the picking hand thumb

# 'Jekyll & Hyde' - Performance Notes

'Jekyll & Hyde', as the name suggests, is a song of two parts: a relaxed, jazz-tinged melody section paired with a more aggressive rock 'Chorus' section. This is one of most popular pieces on the *Renaissance* album and was a key part of Marcus's live set during the subsequent tour.

The song opens with a piano Intro, with the bass joining in after four bars. Marcus plays a simple upper register melody during this section. As ever with Marcus's melodic playing, pay close attention to all slides, hammer-ons and vibrato markings when learning this part as they will really help bring it to life.

At letter B, the heavier rock section begins. This is a harmonically simple two-chord groove that is reminiscent of the funk/soul-edged rock played by Jimi Hendrix, who Marcus reports as being an influence on this part of the song. Under the C7sus4 chord Marcus slaps a C, then plucks the F and B♭ on the D and G-strings, immediately hammering both notes on to the G and C two frets higher. When playing this, I recommend fretting the C on the A-string with the first finger, then using the same finger to barre across the F and B♭. The notes that are hammered-on should then be performed with the fourth finger of the fretting hand, again barring across the two strings. This is how Marcus plays this phrase. The remainder of notes in this bar and the next are slapped with the thumb. This groove features subtle variations each time around: the alternating F's and E♭'s, and the brief slide up to the G♭ in bar 17 are a nice example, as are the alternating C's and A's in bar 19.

At letter C the main melody begins over an A minor-based tonality and Marcus switches to fingerstyle technique. This line features only very small variations each time it repeats. When Marcus plays this piece live, he sometimes uses the palm muting technique for greater contrast during this section.

The remainder of this piece consists of repeats of the grooves discussed above. However, after the final Chorus section (at letter M), Marcus plays what he affectionately refers to as a 'moose call' using his fuzz pedal (bar 117) and the band moves into a new section that is essentially the Chorus part played in the key of the melody section, A minor. Marcus uses his fuzz pedal throughout this section to give the bass part a more aggressive edge. There are some challenging fills using semiquaver triplets in bars 121 and 123: although a lot of notes go by, hammer-ons and pull-offs are used extensively so be sure to follow the slap guides written between the staves when learning these fills. Marcus ends the piece with a brief cadenza using his unique tapping technique, tapping the G at the twelfth fret of the G-string with the edge of the thumb of his picking hand while hammering on and pulling off lower on the string. See the Style Analysis (page 30) for more information on this technique.

# Revelation

**Written by Marcus Miller**

Jazz Rock Ballad ♩. = 130

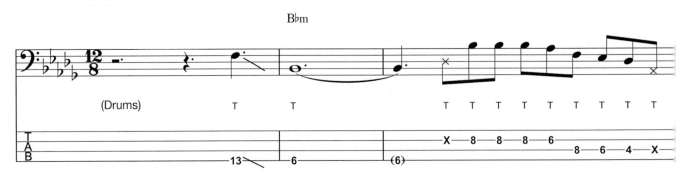

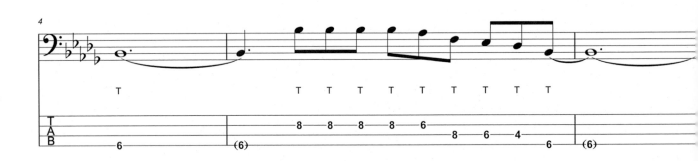

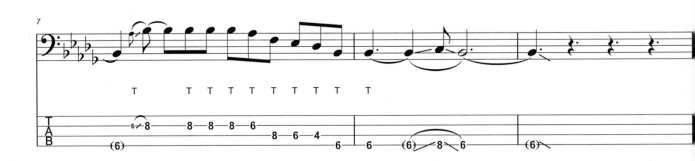

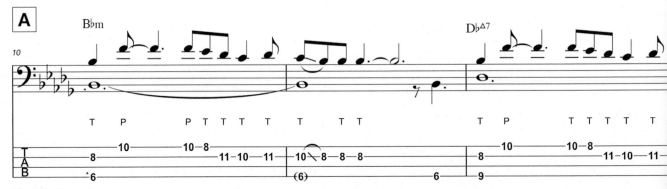

* See performance notes

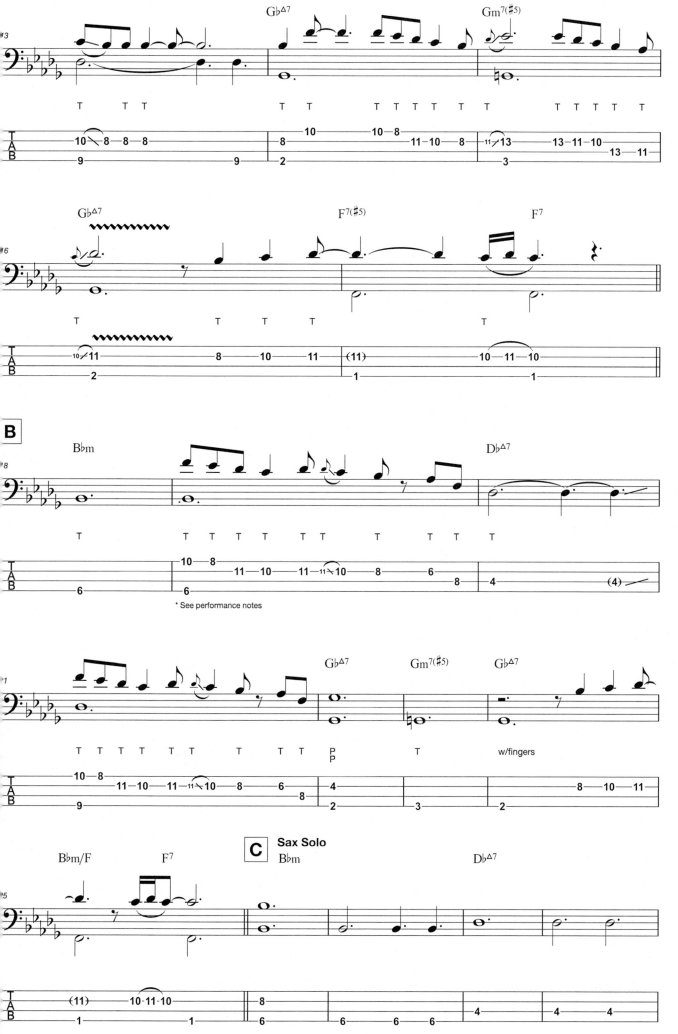

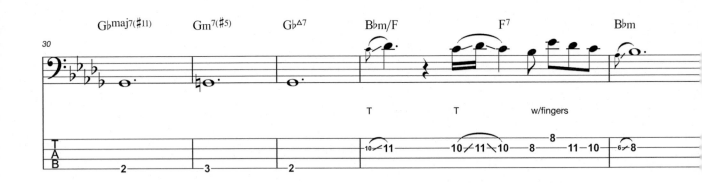
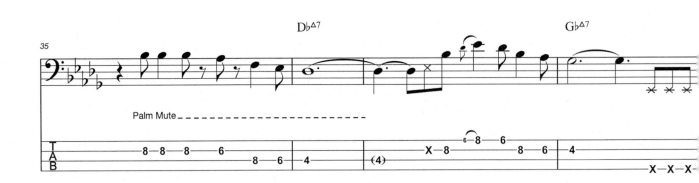
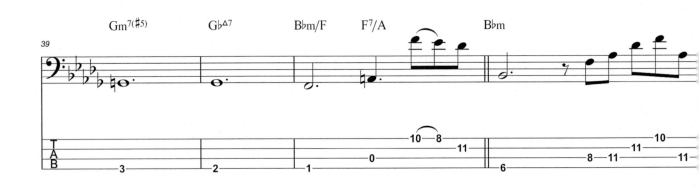

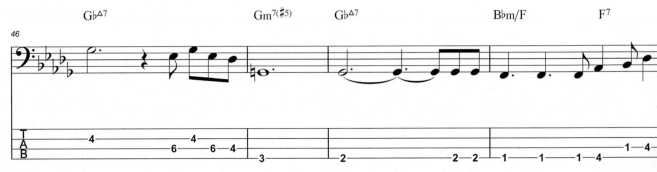

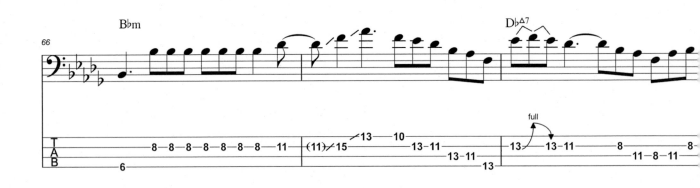

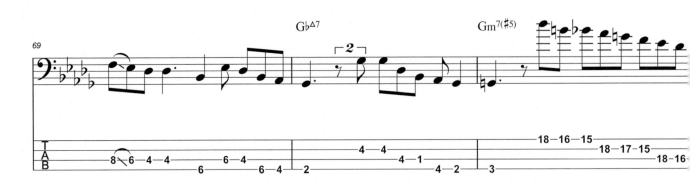

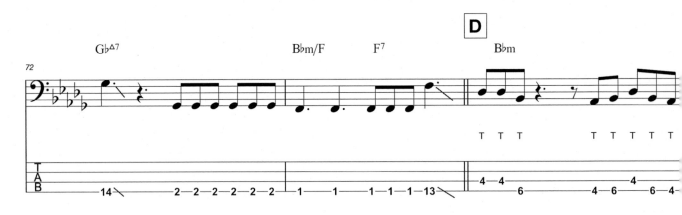

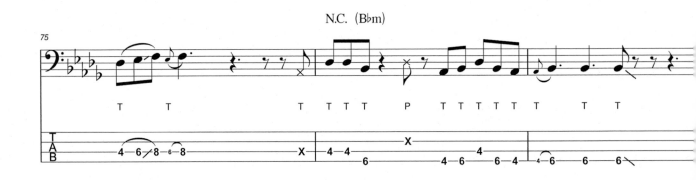

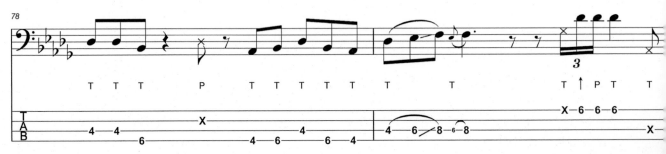

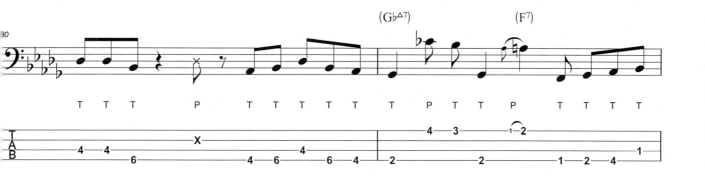
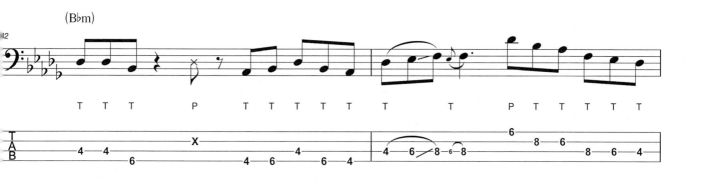
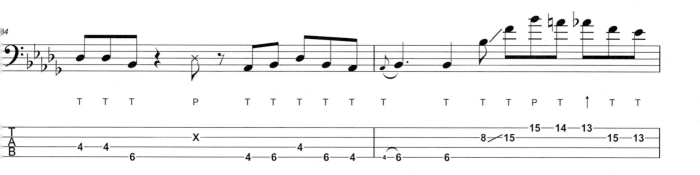
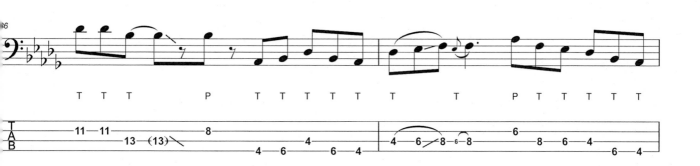
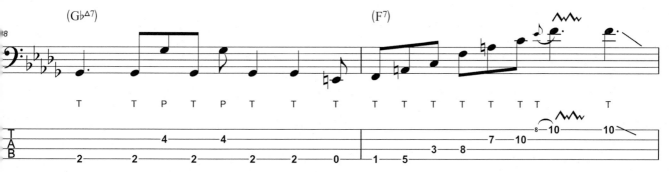

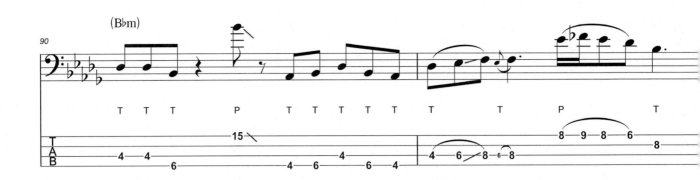

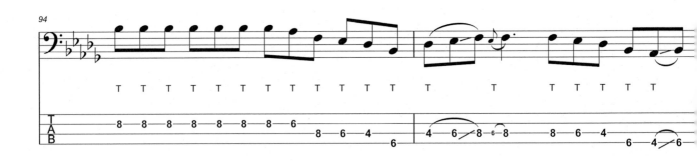

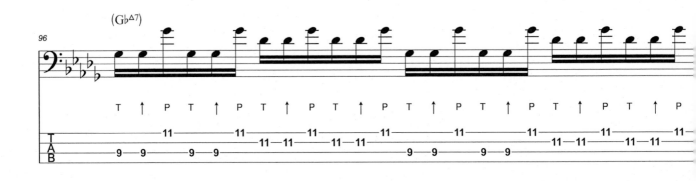

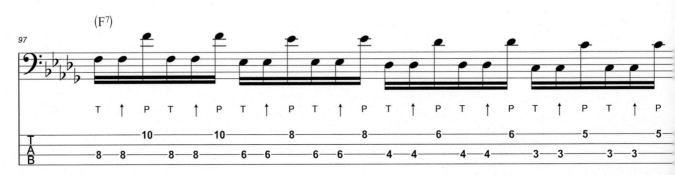

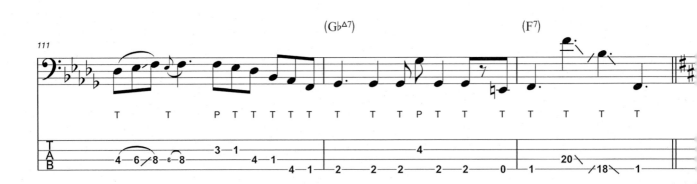

**E**

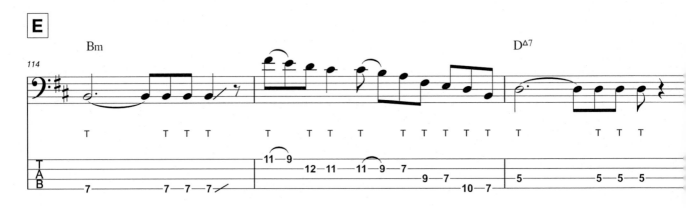

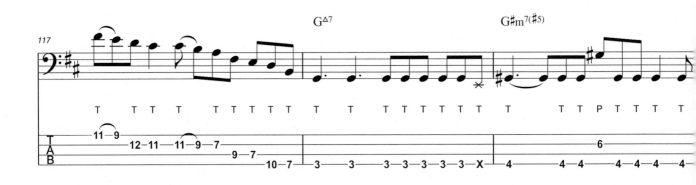

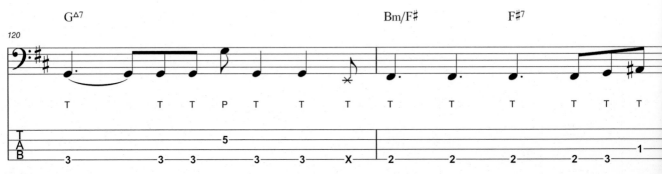

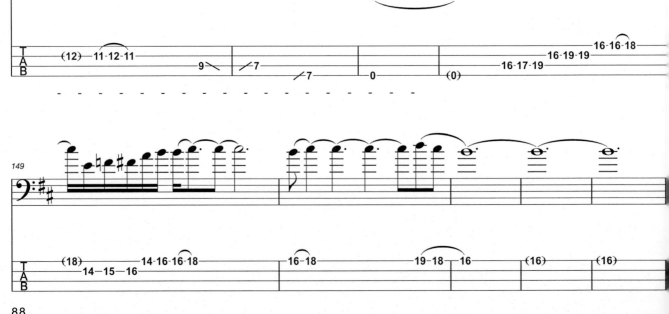

# 'Revelation' - Performance Notes

'Revelation' segues from 'Nocturnal Mist', a piece written by Luther Hanes. Marcus had played this track on bass clarinet for Israel & The New Breed's album *A Timeless Christmas* back in 2006. 'Revelation' was written as a compositional response to this piece and was inspired by saxophonist John Coltrane's work on songs such as 'Alabama' and 'Crescent', which are based around relatively simple minor key progressions.

'Revelation' is a jazz rock ballad in 12/8 time, written in the key of B♭ minor. After an eight bar Intro, during which Marcus slaps B♭ minor pentatonic runs, the main sequence begins at letter A. This is a 12-bar form that is almost entirely diatonic - the exception is the Gm7#5 chord. The F7 chord in the eighth bar of the sequence suggests the harmonic minor scale (which would contain the required A natural), a common move in minor key pieces. At letter A there appear to be two bass parts: one which is the main melody line and another which holds simple bass notes beneath. This second part was most likely overdubbed as the range between the two parts is to large to allow both to be played simultaneously. Marcus plays the melody with the slap technique, with his thumb doing the majority of the work. When playing this melody line, take care to play all slides and slurs (hammer-ons and pull-offs) as notated as they will help with the fluidity of the melody.

Saxophonist Alex Han's solo begins at letter C. Beneath this, Marcus initially plays very simple root-based figures, occasionally adding melodic flourishes such as in bars 33 and 37. From bar 42 onwards his line becomes more active - the Bb minor/minor pentatonic runs in bars 51 and 53 are a nice touch.

At letter D a new movement in the piece begins, with Marcus playing a driving two-bar bass groove. This is slapped entirely with the thumb aside from the slides and hammer-ons in the second bar of the sequence. As the line develops, Marcus begins adding popped notes and

fills, gradually embellishing the simple initial phrase. The tenth intervals in bar 81 are a simple but effective touch, outlining the harmony nicely. Further challenges lie ahead: the wide-ranging F major arpeggio in bar 89 is tough to execute cleanly and will require you to keep your eyes on the fingerboard as you negotiate the wide jumps at this quick tempo. The double thumbed lick beginning in bar 96 however is a little easier than it looks (and sounds): fret a G♭ power chord at the ninth fret position, then play down-up slaps on the root and pop the octave. This is played twice, then the down-up slap movement moves to the fifth of the chord whilst the popped note remains the same. In the second bar of the sequence, you simply play down-up with the thumb on the root, then pop the octave. This figure is then repeated (completing the beat) and moved downwards through the scale. Also of note are the four note groupings in bar 106 - this lick is played with the fingers.

At letter E the piece modulates to B minor and Marcus continues to solo over three further repeats of the chord sequence. The piece ends with a final reading of the main melody section (remaining in the new key of B minor). Marcus plays a free time upper register cadenza in bars 148 - 151.

'Revelation' was regularly performed live during Marcus's tour in support of *Renaissance*. An excellent version recorded with the Metropole Orkest from the Edison Jazz World Awards in 2013 can be seen on YouTube.

# Cee-Tee-Eye

**Written by Marcus Miller**

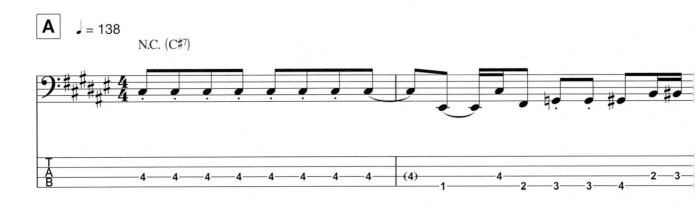

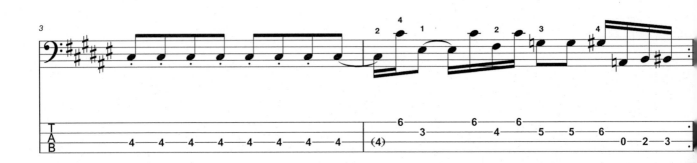

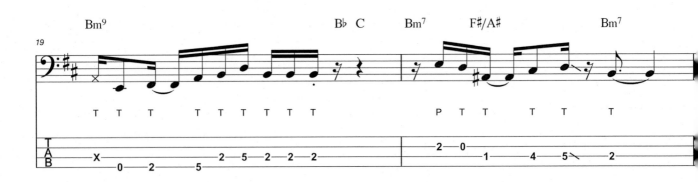

C

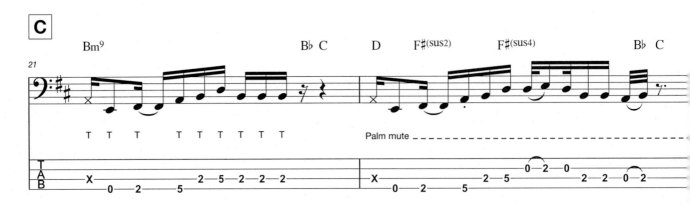

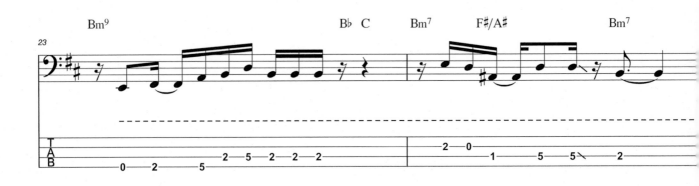

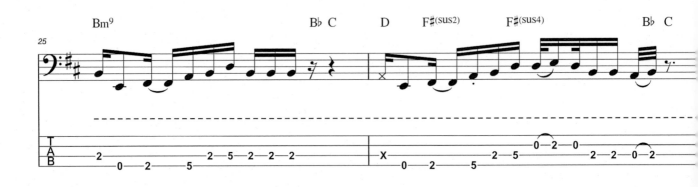

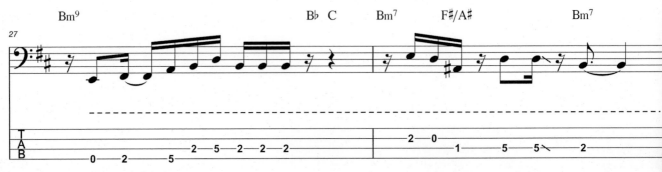

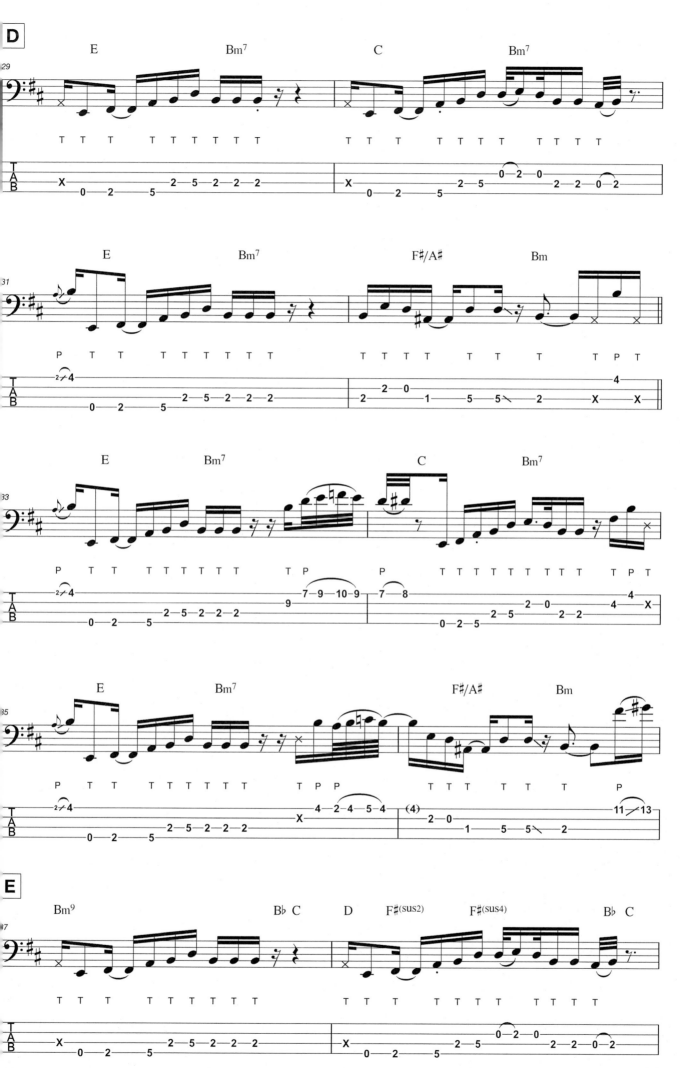

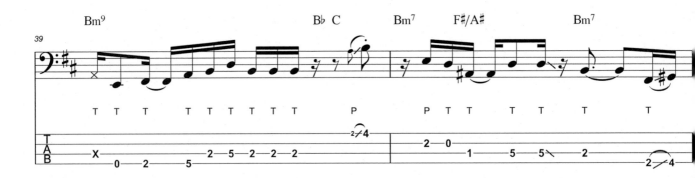

**F** Trumpet Solo

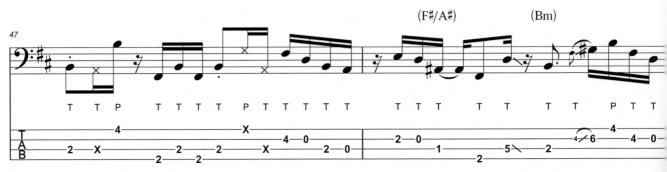

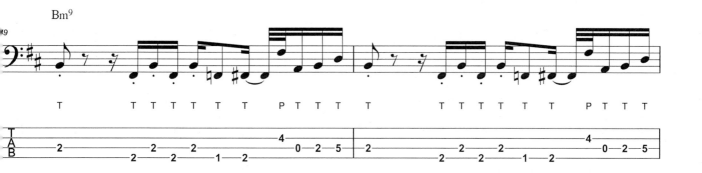
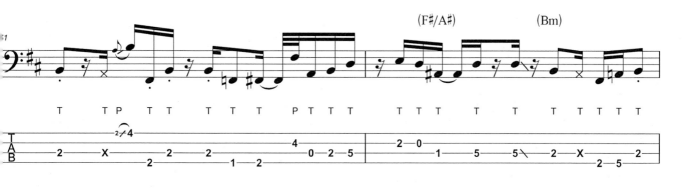

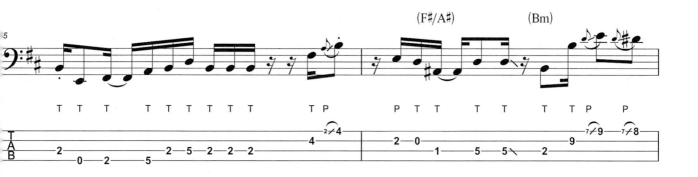
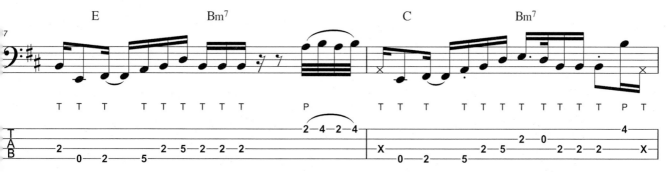

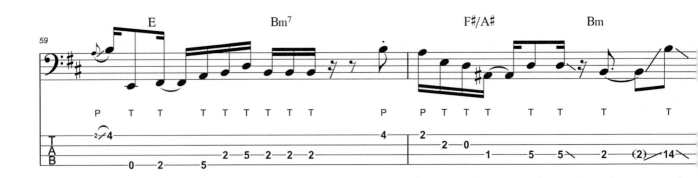

## G Piano Solo

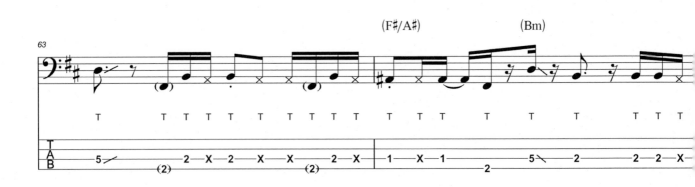

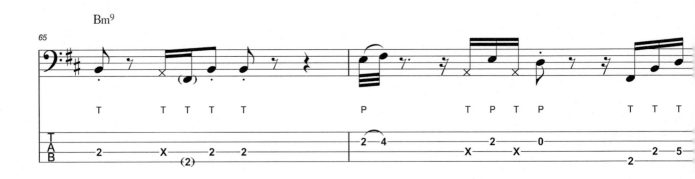

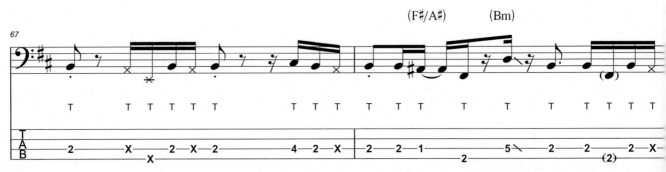

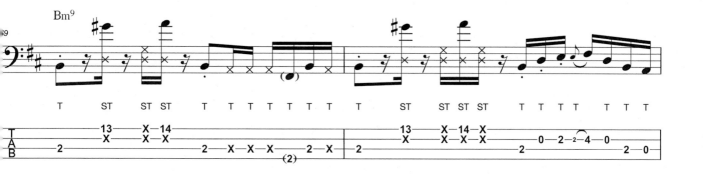

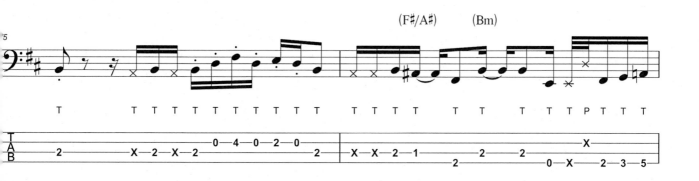
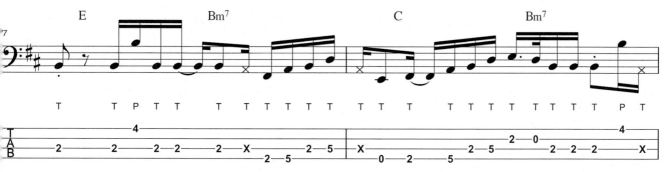

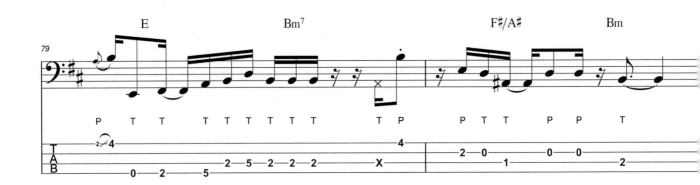

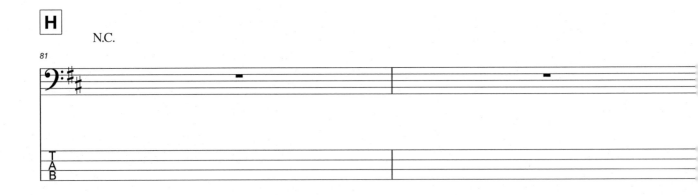

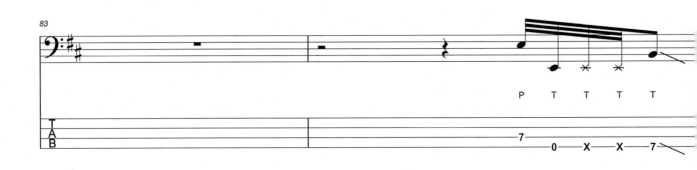

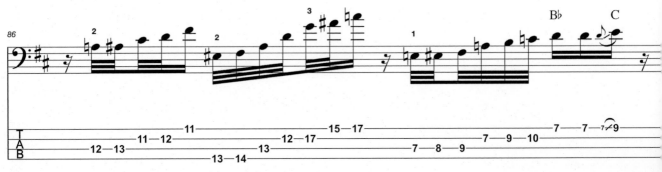

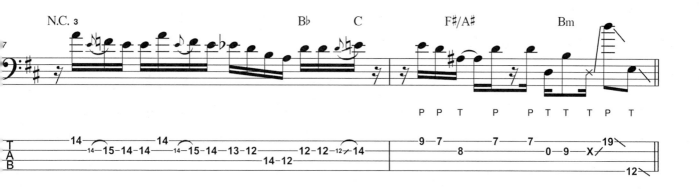

## Bass Solo

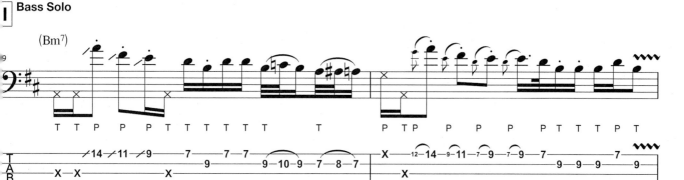

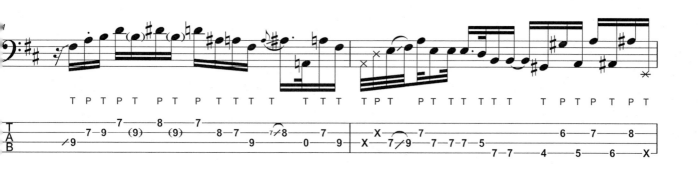

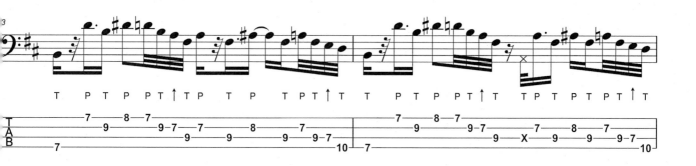

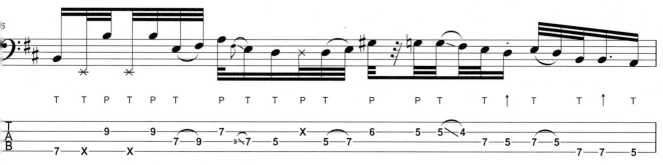

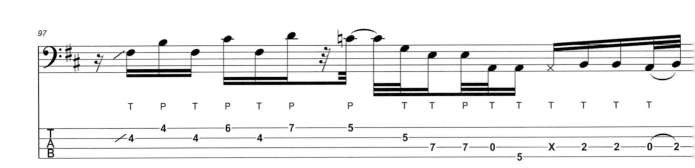

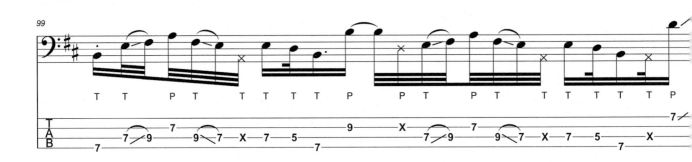

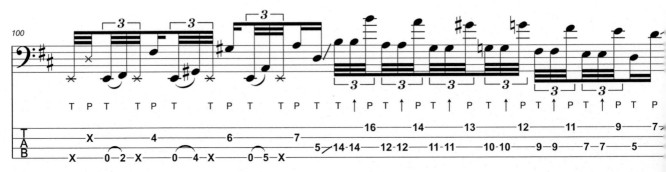

* bend note upwards slightly

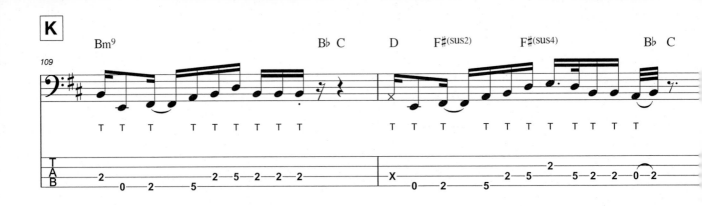

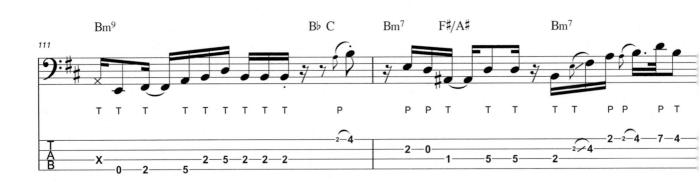

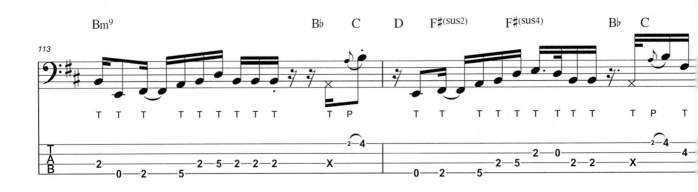

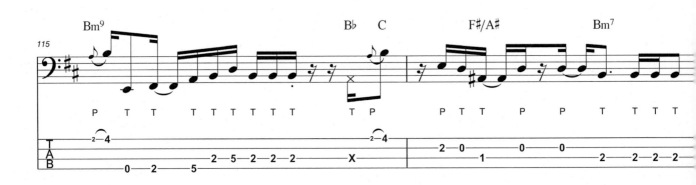

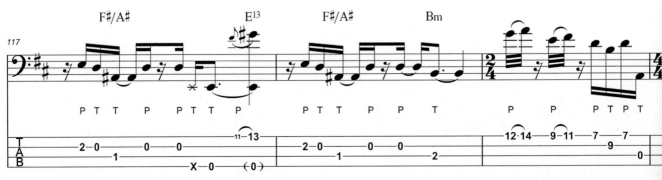

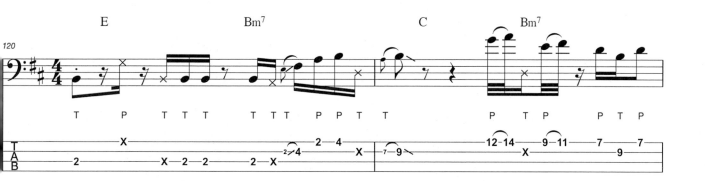

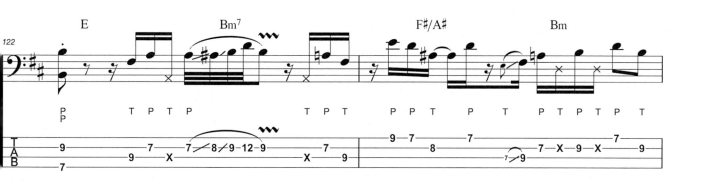

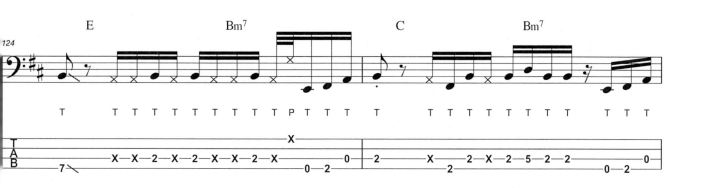

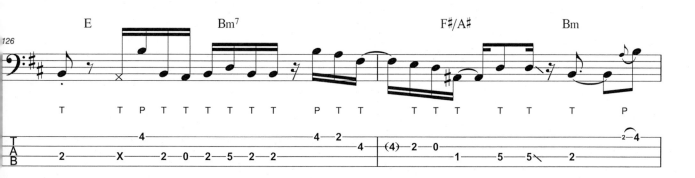

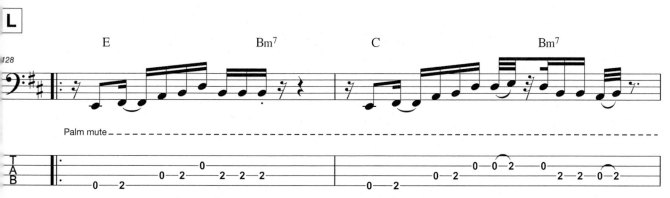

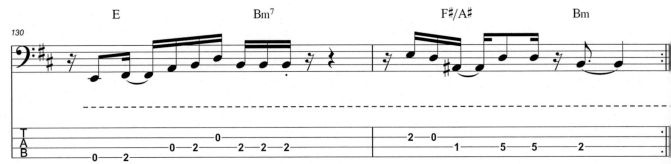

**Repeat sim to fade**

# 'Cee-Tee-Eye' - Performance Notes

**'Cee-Tee-Eye' was written as a nod to CTI Records, the jazz record label founded by producer Creed Taylor and home to many of the artists that Marcus admired growing up. This track has a particularly memorable bass groove as well as some challenging fingerstyle unison riffs and one of Marcus's finest slapped solos.**

The track opens with an Intro section during which Marcus plays a pumping quaver groove with Jamerson-like fills in the second and fourth bars. The line in the fourth bar is particularly challenging at this tempo and I recommend that you fret it using the finger-per-fret technique: with your second finger fretting the C♯ at the fourth fret of the A-string, your other fingers should be in place to play the other notes in the line. In bar 8, Marcus adds another tricky fill, this time an upper register line. Again, I recommend using the finger-per-fret technique: with your fourth finger on the C♯ at the sixteenth fret of the A-string, you should have your fingers in position for the remainder of the line, although you'll need to shift up a fret to play the B♯ at the end of the third beat. These fingerings are indicated above the notes on the score.

At letter B, the tempo drops to half the original speed and the main bass groove begins. This is a four-bar line based around the B natural minor scale and is almost entirely slapped with the thumb. There are many subtle rhythmic variations in this line as it repeats throughout the tune, but don't be put off by the sight of the thirty-second notes - these are much more playable than they look at this relatively slow tempo. This line is used during the melody sections of the song, with Marcus alternating between slap playing and palm muting in response to the overall dynamics of the song.

Despite Marcus's opening double stop chord in bar 41 (which implies a B7 chord), the trumpet solo is played over a B Dorian (Bm7) tonality. Marcus improvises a simple slapped line throughout this part, playing the melodic turnaround phrase from the main groove every four bars. The piano solo is underpinned by a similar groove, which Marcus builds in intensity as the solo builds to its climax.

Following the solos, the horns play a complex unison line at letter H. After the line is played once, Marcus joins in, doubling the part in the upper register. This is a very tricky line to play and again is made easier if you employ the finger-per-fret system in the fretting hand. Once again, recommended fingerings are indicated above the notes on the score.

Marcus's bass solo begins at letter I. For the first four bars he bases his lines around the B minor pentatonic scale, occasionally stepping outside chromatically such as for the D♯ and A♯ notes in bar 91. The first four bars end with an ascending chromatic octave lick from G♯ back up to B. For the next section Marcus alternates between minor and major tenth intervals from B, playing the D and D♯ notes on the G-string. In between phrases he plays a descending minor pentatonic lick (such as on beat 2 of bar 93) which requires a thumb upstroke note - see the double thumbing section of the Style Analysis on page 22 for more information on this technique).

On beat three of bar 95 Marcus plays a figure that begins with two popped notes, followed by a slapped note, all on one string. When playing this phrase you can use both your first and second fingers to pop the notes in sequence, or just one finger. This figure is repeated two further times in the following bar and is a good example of how Marcus will often use thumb slaps and pops for repeated instances of the same note.

In bar 98 Marcus uses one of the triplet techniques discussed in the Style Analysis (page 26). On this occasion the notes are straight thirty-second notes rather than triplets, but played in groups of three. Each grouping begins with a popped open D-string and is followed by a slapped open A-string, then a hammer-on. This technique is quite simple and is good for playing fast licks. Another triplet pattern is employed in bars 100 and 102: this time the technique involves a downstroke with the thumb, followed by an upstroke and a pop. Again, this is easier to apply than it looks (or sounds) and studying Exercises 17 and 18 in the Style Analysis will be a big help when working on these bars.

After the end of Marcus's solo, the unison line with the horns is repeated after which the band repeats the main groove for a final reading of the melody.

This piece is one of the most challenging in the book and will likely take some time to get together. You'll be pleased once you have conquered it though - I know I was.